Exploring
THE SACRAMENTS

ROBERT KELLY

based on the original by
NIGEL BAVIDGE

Kevin
Mayhew

First published in 1999 by
KEVIN MAYHEW LTD
Buxhall
Stowmarket
Suffolk IP14 3BW

0 1 2 3 4 5 6 7 8 9

ISBN 1 84003 376 2
Catalogue No. 1500278

Cover design by Jaquetta Sergeant
Typesetting by Richard Weaver
Printed in Great Britain

CONTENTS

'SACRAMENTS'
Ordinary or sacred?

'Sacrament' is a word which nowadays has an unmistakable religious connotation. Instinctively, people think of 'holy things' or a 'religious ceremony'.

It is true that sacraments have a religious purpose; they are to do with our relationship with God. But the whole point about a 'sacrament' is that it should be fundamentally human, something absolutely ordinary!

Sacraments are delicately balanced between the ordinary world of human experience, and the world of the spiritual – a balance that is not easy to maintain. Too much emphasis on the purely human means we no longer see through and beyond the sacrament to God; too much emphasis on the 'sacredness' of the sacraments means these gestures become remote from the life and experience of people, and equally prevent them from speaking to us of God.

Sacraments, then, are both ordinary and sacred: but they can only become sacred to the extent that they start out by being ordinary. And because they are ordinary, it is only through the eyes of faith that they are seen as sacred.

So what is the 'sacred' that lies behind the sacraments? And why is it that we use the 'ordinary' to reach the 'sacred'? The sacraments concern our relationship with God: since it is with God, we are necessarily in the world of the spiritual, the sacred. But it is a relationship, a two-way dialogue: and since one party to this dialogue (that is to say, you or me!) are human beings, the basic language we use has to be that of our ordinary, everyday experience.

Let's explore this further: first, our relationship with God; and how, since we are human beings, this relationship is expressed.

OUR RELATIONSHIP WITH GOD

What does God want of us and for us? 'God wants everyone to be saved and reach full knowledge of the truth' (1 Timothy 2:4). With this deceptively simple sentence Saint Paul sums up the meaning of life. For a Christian, everything else should lead to this single and ultimate goal.

'God wants everyone to be saved . . .' Saved from what and why?

The mystery of creation

We are thrown back to the first great mystery of humankind's relationship with God: creation. Confronted with the eternal question, 'Where do we come from?' the Bible offers not an *explanation*, but, through the eyes of faith, an *interpretation*: we are sons and daughters of God because we owe our very existence to God. We are, in the metaphor of Genesis, the work of his hands. Or to quote the key phrase from the opening chapter of Genesis we are 'made in the image and likeness of God'.

We have here a fundamental act of faith: you want to see God? Sorry, this is beyond human experience – but, for those who know how to look with the eyes of faith, glimpses are possible. And faith boldly declares that the first place to look is at yourself, for you are made in the image and likeness of God.

Faith is not blinded by the wonders of creation, however. We cannot close our eyes to our 'dark' side. This particular aspect is explored more fully in the chapter on reconciliation (see pages 61-80). For the moment, let us note that the great hymn in praise of creation which opens the Bible is immediately followed by the dramatic story of the 'Fall'. Because we are made in

God's image we are free – which includes the freedom to say to God, 'We think we can manage fine without you.'

The mystery of salvation

So begins the second great mystery, the mystery of the 'salvation' offered by God which means that, in complete respect of the freedom he gave us, God calls us to come back to him, to make the free choice of opting to follow his way, rather than our own

However, all of this, even if it comes from God, needs to come in ways and through means that are accessible to humankind: the message may come from God, but it is human beings who need to be able to hear it! In this sense, the whole of the history of salvation is coloured by creation. In the Garden of the Genesis story, God talks directly with Adam and with Eve. Once they have been expelled from the Garden, the dialogue is no longer direct, it has to be mediated through people and/or events.

So it is that, as the Letter to the Hebrews puts it, 'At various times in the past and in various different ways, God spoke through the prophets . . .' (Hebrews 1:1).

The Bible presents the first mystery of creation in a couple of chapters. The second mystery, that of redemption, of being reconciled with God, occupies every other page of the Bible!

It is important to see how these two mysteries intersect and come together: the mystery of creation was not, *is* not undone by humankind's abuse of God-given freedom. Distorted perhaps, but not undone. The second mystery, that of redemption, grows out of and is determined by the first mystery of creation: *creation* (which makes us what we are) dictates what *redemption* (for us as we are) must mean.

The mystery of the incarnation

This gives birth to a third mystery: in order that humankind might be reconciled to God, God accepts humanity. In order that we may rediscover fully our nature 'in the image and likeness of God', God accepts fully to be in the image and likeness of humankind. So we have the mystery of the incarnation: '. . . in our own time, God has spoken to us through his Son' (Hebrews 1:1). Or as John's Gospel expresses it, stressing that the word is more than a message: 'The Word was made flesh and lived among us'. In fact, the original Greek uses very down-to-earth and ordinary language: 'He pitched his tent among us' (John 1:14). Luke's Gospel makes the link between the prophets and Jesus explicit, by showing how he fulfils the promises made by Isaiah: he is anointed by the Holy Spirit, to preach the Good News to the poor, to proclaim liberty to captives, to give sight to the blind, to set the downtrodden free . . . (cf. Luke 4:18 and Isaiah 61:1).

We already noted that in Old Testament times, God's message for his people was mediated by events as well as by the preaching of the prophets. So too in the life of Jesus, the Good News is proclaimed as much by what he *does* as by what he *says*.

The paschal mystery

Jesus' life's work was to bring people back to the Father; but it is above all in what we call **the paschal mystery** that Jesus redeems humanity and offers perfect praise and glory to God: in other words it is by his death and resurrection, and his ascension: 'Dying he destroyed our death, rising he restored our life . . .'

The history of Christianity is full of examples of attempts which explore the two great mysteries, the mystery of creation and the mystery of redemption. The best examples are those which seek to relate the two, and explore this by comparing and contrasting the symbols by which these mysteries are expressed: the tree in the garden with the wood of the cross; Adam's disobedience with Christ's obedience. In fact, the comparison in these examples is more between the fall and redemption.

There is another very evocative parallel between the mystery of creation – and in particular Eve being created from the side of Adam – and the mystery of salvation through Christ's death on the cross. We find this parallel expressed by Saint Augustine, but also by other Fathers of the Church such as John Chrysostom.

John Chrysostom, speaking to the candidates who are preparing to receive baptism and Eucharist for the first time at the paschal vigil, makes the parallel explicit:

'The Gospel relates that when Christ had died and was still hanging on the cross, the soldier approached him and pierced his side with the spear, and at once there came out water and blood. The one was the symbol of baptism, the other of the Eucharist . . . the symbols of baptism and the Eucharist came from his side. It was from his side, then, that Christ formed the Church, as from the side of Adam he formed Eve . . . As God took the rib from Adam while Adam was in a deep sleep, so now he gave the blood and water after his death.' (John Chrysostom, *3rd Instruction to Catechumens.*)

Saint Augustine is more direct: 'It was from the side of Christ as he slept the sleep of death on the cross that there came forth the sacrament which is the whole Church.' (Saint Augustine, *Commentary on Psalm 138.*)

'God wants everyone to be saved . . .' (1 Timothy 2:4). Here lies the origin, the meaning and the purpose of Christ's life, death and resurrection – and thereafter of the Church and of the sacraments which flow from Christ's paschal mystery.

FROM 'MYSTERY' TO 'SACRAMENT'

In the introductory section, we used the word 'sacrament'. However, in our exploration of the sacred that lies behind the sacraments, the word we used was 'mystery'.

Two key words: 'mystery' and 'sacrament'. In fact they are two ways of referring to the same reality: one, 'mystery', derived from Greek; the other, 'sacrament', from Latin.

'Mystery'

The language of the first Christians was Greek, so they used the word 'mystery'. In ordinary everyday language nowadays, a mystery is something we cannot fully understand – but the emphasis is put on the part that is not understandable, so much so that to call something a mystery is to say it is a puzzle without a solution.

The original force of the word 'mystery', however, was the opposite! The emphasis was on what it *did* permit us to grasp, however incompletely, however obliquely. This is what Paul meant in his famous expression 'We see, but as in a dim reflection in a mirror' (1 Corinthians 13:12). Notice he does not say we *cannot* see; yes, he admits we cannot see completely, nor clearly, but we can still see something.

A mystery, in this sense, is something you can look at and understand at first level; but beyond that, a mystery launches you towards perceiving something that is imperceptible. A letter from a fiancé to his fiancée can be read by anyone; however, the recipient will read between the lines and perceive, sense and feel the love which paper and ink cannot really carry.

'Mystery', then, was the word that the Church adopted to denote symbolic acts, gestures, words and things which in themselves were ordinary but to the eyes of faith spoke of 'salvation' and opened a way to a fuller 'understanding of the truth'.

'Salvation' and 'truth' are rather abstract concepts. In fact, it is quite clear from the New Testament that for the early Christians the 'mystery' was the person who is the source of salvation and truth, that is Christ himself. (See the quotes in the column to the right.)

When we explore all the uses of 'mystery' in the New Testament, it is clear that the constant underlying reference is to the unfathomable action of God in wanting to save everyone, referring especially to the way that salvation is made visible, audible, and accessible, but above all real and present in Christ. There are, then, three essential elements in what can be called a sacrament:

- salvation
- made visible, but above all realised and made present
- in Christ.

Beyond referring to Christ himself, 'mystery' was used of the words but above all the actions of Christ because these were spoken and accomplished in order to achieve our salvation and bring us back to the Father. Similarly, 'mystery' was used of the Church; in time, the expression 'mysteries' in the plural was used particularly of the two Eucharistic symbols of bread and wine.

'Sacrament'

When the language of the ordinary people was no longer Greek but Latin, the Church followed this change. So it is with Tertullian (writing around the year AD 200, in North Africa): he chose the word '*sacramentum*', which gives us the English word 'sacrament'. It was a very ingenious choice – not a direct translation – because of the meaning that *sacramentum* already had.

Sacramentum meant the oath of allegiance that a Roman soldier swore to his legion and thereby to the emperor (considered, remember, as a god): it was a solemn promise, a public declaration of surrendering oneself to the service of another. Further, legionaries were marked with a branding iron to show which legion they belonged to. In other words, they bore a physical, visible mark which bore witness to the promise made and the relationship established by that promise. All of this conveyed by one single word!

This richness of meaning was appropriated by Tertullian when he chose 'sacrament' to speak of the way baptism, confirmation and the Eucharist (the sacraments of initiation) mark a person for life as belonging to Christ. The water, the oil, the bread and the wine were all visible – as was the brand stamped on a legionary. But beyond the physical mark, they symbolised the Christian entrusting himself or herself to death with Christ in baptism with the promise of rising again with him.

As the life of the Church became more organised in the third, fourth and fifth centuries, the word 'sacrament' was applied more broadly than just to Christ himself. We have already seen the quote from Saint Augustine, for example, where he says the Church is a 'sacrament'. But the underlying reference to the saving paschal mystery of Christ remains constant.

We know that as late as the eleventh century, the word 'sacrament' was in ordinary usage, meaning a solemn, irrevocable promise. (See the tableau from the Bayeux Tapestry below.)

The accompanying text clearly proclaims **Harold sacramentum fecit**: literally, *Harold performed a sacrament*, meaning he swore a solemn and public promise. As late as the eleventh century, then, the word 'sacrament' simply meant a solemn, irrevocable public promise.

In this tableau from the Bayeux Tapestry we see Harold Godwineson swearing an oath of fealty to William, Duke of Normandy (in 1064 or 1065).

SEVEN 'SACRAMENTS'

For over a thousand years of Christianity, the word 'sacrament' was used generally to refer to symbolic actions, performed or ministered by the Church in the name of Christ. They were always actions, but actions involving visible symbols. It is only in the Middle Ages, the great era of Scholastic theology, that seven symbolic actions are singled out to be described as 'sacraments' in a privileged way.

Why, at this moment in history, did the word 'sacrament' come to be defined in a narrower sense, restricted to seven? The spirit of the times was to clarify by classifying, by organising and sorting things into systems.

So for these great medieval theologians the key question, as far as the sacraments were concerned, was: among all the things that are or have been called 'sacraments', which of them speak unambiguously about Christ and his mission of bringing salvation to all? This came down to looking for three essential qualities – all of which had to be present – for something to be 'a sacrament':

– do they make memory of Christ's saving work?

– do they demonstrate clearly by their very nature what aspect of that salvation is accomplished in us here and now?

– do they prefigure the salvation promised to us?

Notice how, implicitly in this, sacraments are seen to transcend time: rooted in Christ in the past, used by us and affecting us today, and opening the way to eternal life with God that is yet to come.

The Scholastic theologians identified seven symbolic sets of actions and words which met these demanding criteria: baptism, confirmation, Eucharist, penance, anointing of the sick, matrimony and ordination.

The work of these theologians was adopted by the Church and became the Church's official teaching. At the Second Council of Lyons (1274), and in the *Decretum pro Armenis* of the Council of Florence (1439), the doctrine was officially declared that there were seven sacraments, seven privileged ways of being caught up and sharing in the salvation gained once and for all by Christ through his death, but made available through space and through time by the ministry of the Church.

In what sense are the sacraments 'privileged'? They are 'privileged' in the sense that these are understood as coming from Christ himself, or as the technical language has it 'instituted by the Lord'. 'Privileged' also in the sense that they are saving actions in which Christ himself is present. 'Privileged' in the sense that through them, we find salvation in Christ. The technical word for this saving presence of Christ and its effect on us is 'grace'. Each sacrament offers a specific 'grace' as signified and symbolised by the material elements of the sacrament.

There is no doubt that it was out of the deepest possible respect that the Scholastics set out these privileged sacraments which effected what they symbolised : unfortunately, in practice, this gave rise to the oversimple interpretation that 'sacraments always work', which led to them being celebrated in the most ridiculous ways. The example (see chapter on confirmation, page 37) of the bishop arriving in a village and administering confirmation without even getting down from his horse is, unfortunately, only one of many examples that could be quoted.

It was the experience of this type of very poor pastoral practice which led Luther to re-examine this doctrine of there being seven sacraments – a doctrine which, in relative terms was fairly recent. Using as the central criterion that a sacrament had to be a saving word and action, given to us by Christ himself, Luther concluded that there were only two unambiguous sacraments instituted by Christ: baptism and the Eucharist.

In its work of countering the errors of the Reformation, the Council of Trent (1547) reiterated that there are seven sacraments: baptism, confirmation or chrismation, Eucharist, penance, anointing of the sick, holy orders and matrimony.

CHRIST *THE* SACRAMENT

Of course the Second Vatican Council re-echoes this fundamental doctrine that 'in the liturgy the sanctification of men and women is manifested by signs perceptible to the senses and is effected in a way which is proper to each of these signs' (SC 7).

What is 'new' about Vatican II is its rediscovery and its development of how this is effected and therefore how the sacraments should be celebrated.

At the heart of this lies the fundamental truth that Christ is the primordial sacrament. He alone in his death and resurrection is the full and effective sign of our salvation; that thereafter, the Church itself is 'sacrament' in being Christ's body for the world of today; the Church is the universal sacrament, making the primordial sacrament of Christ present throughout time and space.

These two key ideas are then unpacked, to give several consequences, which are both theological (about the meaning of the sacraments) and practical (how they should be celebrated).

Sacraments as actions of Christ

The first key consequence is that the sacraments are always **actions of Christ**. In a very literal sense, they are rooted in an experience recounted in the New Testament, where Christ himself entrusts a symbolic action (words, gestures and sign) to his apostles. The clearest example is in the Eucharist: Christ takes, breaks, blesses and shares bread and wine, and commands, 'Do this . . .'. But it is true for all the sacraments, as the individual chapters show.

In a deeper sense, the sacraments are always actions of Christ, because all the sacraments make present and effective Christ in his dying and rising again: they make present the paschal mystery.

Relatedly, the sacraments are always actions of Christ because they are performed by the body of Christ, which is the Church.

Sacraments as encounters with Christ

There is a second key idea, which is a consequence of these first two: for those who take part in the celebration of a sacrament, it is nothing less than a personal encounter with Christ, made possible through the ministry of the Church. If it is a personal encounter, it is an encounter between Christ and each of us, as we are, with our human freedom. This presence of Christ, sometimes referred to as 'grace', is not forced upon us: it is offered. A sacrament can only be a sacrament for those who respond freely and in faith.

If sacraments are encounters with Christ, they ought to be opportunities where Christ can speak to us! This is why all sacraments have a liturgy of the Word, where the Gospel is proclaimed. Sometimes this may be short (as in the reconciliation celebrated with just the priest and the penitent); sometimes this may be very long (as in the Easter Vigil, preparing for the three sacraments of baptism, confirmation and Eucharist). Always, it should include a sharing of the Gospel, Christ's Word proclaimed aloud.

Meeting Christ by being Christ

There is a third key idea, which strikes a balance between the first and second: sacraments are personal encounters with Christ, but they are not private and individual. The way in which Christ is present is through his body, the Church, head and members. It is as 'Church' that we find Christ in the sacraments, it is as 'Church' that his presence is made real in the world of today. So,

'Liturgical services are not private functions, but are celebrations belonging to the Church, which is the sacrament of unity, namely the holy people united and ordered under their bishops.

'Therefore liturgical services involve the whole body of the Church; they manifest it and have effects upon it; but they also concern the individual members of the Church in different ways, according to their different orders, offices and actual participation.' (SC 26)

This is why Vatican II encouraged and restored active participation: the world of the liturgy and of the sacraments is one of symbols. But always the symbol should represent as unambiguously as possible what it symbolises and signifies: in order that it be clear that Christ is present and active in each sacrament, his body – head and members – should be visibly at work in the sacrament. A sacrament can only happen, then, in the context of the Church, in the context of an assembly of the baptised coming together in faith with their ordained pastor.

This does not mean that everybody should do everything, although there are some symbolic moments when that is the case. (All should take equal part in the acclamations during the eucharistic prayer, for example.) What it does mean is that each should play his or her appropriate part. Not everyone has the talent to read scripture aloud; even among those who do, they cannot all read at once. Sometimes, then, the full, conscious and active participation that is demanded will be that of listening: apparently 'passive', it should be an active reception of the word of God.

Exploring the sacraments

The title of this book is *Exploring the sacraments*. One of the essential characteristics of sacraments is that they are 'celebrated', they are the very heart of liturgy. In that sense, the best way to explore sacraments is to celebrate them, to let the sacraments speak for themselves.

What can be explored is how these words and actions are founded on words and actions entrusted to us by Christ. We can also explore the way in which Christians across the ages have worked to shape the celebration of the sacraments, so that they can speak to those who take part in the celebration. Which is why every chapter in this book offers a historical perspective on each of the sacraments.

To write a book about sacraments, to have discussion groups about them in the parish – all this is useful, important even, but always secondary.

Sacraments cannot be 'explained', per-haps they cannot even be 'explored'. Sacraments can only be 'celebrated'.

This is why each chapter in this book dedicates so much space to the current official texts from each of the sacraments. In celebrating the sacraments we are expressing the most profound of our beliefs: the words from the rites in which we do this, but especially the gestures that accompany these words, are far more eloquent than any commentary.

> *'Just as Christ was sent by the Father, so too he sent the apostles, filled with the Holy Spirit. He did this in order that the apostles, by preaching the gospel to all [Mark 16:15], would proclaim that the Son of God, by his death and resurrection, had freed us from the power of Satan [Acts 26:18] and from death and brought us into the kingdom of the Father. His purpose was also that they might exercise the work of salvation, which they were proclaiming, by means of sacrifice and sacraments around which the whole liturgical life revolves . . .*
>
> *To accomplish so great a work, Christ is always present in his Church, especially in her liturgical celebrations . . . Christ always associates the Church with himself in the truly great work of giving perfect praise to God and making all holy.'*
>
> **(SC 6 and 7)**

THE LITURGY AS DEFINED IN CANON LAW

Canon. 834 §1 The Church carries out its office of sanctifying in a special way in the sacred liturgy, which is an exercise of the priestly office of Jesus Christ. In the liturgy, by the use of signs perceptible to the senses, our sanctification is symbolised and, in a manner appropriate to each sign, is brought about. Through the liturgy a complete public worship is offered to God by the head and members of the mystical body of Christ.

Canon. 837 §1 Liturgical actions are not private but are celebrations of the Church itself as the 'sacrament of unity', that is, the holy people united and ordered under the Bishops. Accordingly, they concern the whole body of the Church, making it known and influencing it. They affect individual members of the Church in ways that vary according to orders, role and actual participation.

§2 Since liturgical matters by their very nature call for a community celebration, they are, as far as possible, to be celebrated in the presence of Christ's faithful and with their active participation.

BAPTISM
*Life . . . and **new** life*

CELEBRATING A NEW LIFE

Almost without exception, the birth of a baby is a source of great happiness for families. It is an occasion of joy, pride and excitement – and a great sense of relief.

The new baby soon becomes the focus of attention not just for the mother and father, but for other relatives and friends who come to inspect the new arrival.

The 'new' parents inevitably have a great sense of pride – tinted with certain apprehensions about the new responsibilities they have acquired. They are full of dreams and ambitions for their child. Many of these hopes remain unspoken and many are unlikely to be fulfilled. Underlying the various dreams there is one fundamental hope which parents have for their child: they want their child to be happy, to grow up good, honest and fulfilled. They want their child to grow up to achieve his or her potential, to grow up to be a worthwhile person.

In our Christian culture, one of the first decisions that the parents have to make about their child concerns baptism: should we have our baby baptised? Many do ask that their baby be baptised, and lying behind such a request there is often a whole mixture of motives:

- it may be a family tradition, so the parents feel the new baby 'ought' to be baptised

- sometimes this tradition can take the form of pressure from the family

- some people seem to regard baptism as something like a lucky charm; they want to feel that their baby will have God on his or her side

- for others, it is simply an elaborate way of giving the baby a name, and a good excuse for a party!

Reasons like this frequently lie behind the request to have a baby baptised. They spring from family concerns and concerns for the baby – but are they good enough reasons? Do they really take into account what having a baby baptised implies?

In other words, a measured judgement about having a baby baptised, as well as considering the baby and the family, needs also to consider what baptism means. Parents ought to ask themselves:

- what is baptism?

- why do we think baptism is important for our child?

- what are our real reasons for wanting our child baptised?

- what does having our baby baptised mean? what does it mean for the baby? for us as parents? for the church, which offers baptism?

- what are the implications of having our baby baptised: for us and for our baby?

These are wide-ranging and important questions which cannot be properly answered unless we have first explored the meaning and purpose of life. Normally the request for baptism comes from parents who belong to a Christian tradition – though their relation with the church may be more, or less active. It is from this Christian aspect that our exploration should begin: how do Christians understand life?

As Christians, we believe that life comes from God. We believe also that as human beings we will die, but that death only changes this life, it does not bring it to an end.

Christians believe that beyond our human experience of mortality and limitation, all human life is eternal; we are born to live for ever. This means that Christians take an overview of human existence: our life here on earth is just the beginning which should lead to life with God for ever.

In trying to understand this, Christians quite naturally refer to Christ. Here is how

Jesus, speaking to his friends the night before he himself will be put to death, understands the end of his human life:

I am going now
to prepare a place for you,
and after I have gone and prepared a
*   place,*
I shall return to take you with me,
so that where I am
you may be too.
(John 14:3)

'I am going . . .' Jesus says. The metaphor implicit behind these reassuring words is that life is a journey. We have come from God, we believe; so too we are called to return to him. Life is a journey – but where are we to find the map that will guide us on this journey? In the continuation of what he says to his disciples that night, Jesus offers a simple but astonishing reply:

I am the Way ...
no one can come to the Father
except through me.
(John 14:6)

Jesus goes before us, but in two senses: the first sense is that as Christians, we become followers of Jesus, who has shown us the way to live and journey safely through life. But if this is all Jesus meant, he could have said 'I know the way and I will show it to you'.

What Jesus says is far more profound. He says not just 'here is the way', but 'I am the way'. The way is not just in following Christ, not just in being like Christ, but in **becoming** Christ.

Christ is not simply a leader who shows the way. As we journey through life, he promises to be with us, not on the way, but **as** the Way. This means that there is not a single step on this journey that Christ is not with us. This means we know, with certainty, that for those who accept to undertake it, this journey will end in and with Christ.

Baptism is the first step on this journey: it is the moment of commitment to be in and with Christ.

CELEBRATING NEW LIFE

Baptism is the public ceremony by which we commit ourselves, or our parents on our behalf commit us, to set out on this journey into and with Christ to God.

Already, then, baptism implies that God invites us home to him. This invitation, this call from God to us to come back and live with him for ever is called 'faith'.

Faith, then, it is not a thing, it is a relationship. Just as a baby does not ask to be born, but is the fruit of his or her parents' love, so too, eternal life from God is offered in love from God as a gift.

Already, then, we should note that baptism is not a right, but a privilege, or rather it is the privileged promise of a gift and that gift is a relationship with God.

What kind of relationship? In primitive religions we find that the relationship is one of weak slaves to an all powerful master. For Abraham and the Jewish people who are his successors, their relationship is radically different: they are the people of God. The word that they use in Hebrew for 'faith' indicates how they understood this relationship: the root meaning is 'to lean upon'.

Jesus was to take this gentle, homely image of strong confidence and express it in one word. He dared to call God 'Abba'. 'Abba' is an Aramaic word – but it has its equivalent in every known language. It is the simplest of words, the equivalent of a baby saying something like 'Papa' or 'Dada', with the unquestioning trust of a baby towards his or her father: this is what faith means.

Faith is the trusting answer we make to God in response to his invitation to be his children. But already, as Christians, we believe that we have life from God. Is not every living person a child of God? In a sense, yes. But that is the life, as brothers of Adam and sisters of Eve, the mortal life that will end with death. God calls us beyond death to life with him, the life as brothers and sisters of Christ, eternal life as children of God.

JOINING CHRIST IN HIS BODY

Yet again, we find Christ at the centre of the meaning of life. If by baptism we are in and with Christ, then we are – like him – sons and daughters of God.

Baptism is this 'incorporation into Christ' which means literally 'joining Christ in his body'.

This has two meanings – both of which are the consequence of baptism.

The first meaning of joining Christ in his body means being nailed with him to the cross: not literally, although it does mean that we will die. But in accepting baptism we are declaring publicly, and in advance, that we associate our own inevitable death with the death of Christ. However, we do so in order to pass, with Christ, through death to the Father. Saint Paul expresses it with unambiguous clarity:

> *When we were baptised*
> *we were baptised in his death.*
> *In other words,*
> *when we were baptised*
> *we went into the tomb with him*
> *and joined him in death,*
> *so that as Christ was raised*
> *from the dead*
> *by the Father's glory,*
> *we too might live a new life.*
> *We believe that having died*
> *with Christ*
> *we shall return to life with him.*
>
> *(Romans 6:4-8)*

Baptism means deliberately associating ourselves – or our child, if we are presenting a baby for baptism – with Christ's death, but so as to be associated with him in his resurrection.

Let us go back to that eloquent metaphor of faith as meaning 'leaning on'. Baptism means accepting the gift of faith from God. Even death – Christ has shown us – should hold no fear for us: it is, to eyes of faith, simply going to sleep in the arms of God, in the assuring knowledge that it is God who will waken us and make us get up to the new and unending day with him in heaven.

There is a second meaning to 'joining Christ in his body'. Again we are indebted to Saint Paul for his clear presentation:

> *Just as a human body,*
> *though it is made up of*
> *many parts,*
> *is a single unit*
> *because all these parts,*
> *though many,*
> *make one body,*
> *so it is with Christ.*
> *In the one Spirit we were*
> *all baptised . . .*
> *Now you together are*
> *Christ's body:*
> *but each of you is a different*
> *part of it.*
>
> *(1 Corinthians 12:12-27)*

In baptism we join Christ's body which is the Church – the 'body' of people who are entrusted with continuing Christ's presence and work in the world.

Baptism, then, is 'incorporation in Christ'. We shall discover in our exploration of baptism that the various symbolic things used in baptism (water, a candle, a white garment) all express, in one way or another, this same underlying theme: in baptism, we die with Christ so as to rise with him. Baptism, so often a celebration of a new life, is – more importantly – a celebration of the new life that God offers us as brothers and sisters of Christ.

This is the fundamental meaning of baptism. To understand this meaning more fully, and to grasp clearly the implications of baptism, we need to explore how it has been presented in the New Testament, and how it has been presented by the church across the centuries.

BAPTISM IN THE GOSPELS

Matthew's Gospel introduces Christ to us by way of two short chapters (out of a total of 28 chapters) which cover his birth and infancy. Similarly in Luke there are two introductory chapters (out of 24) which cover not only the birth of Jesus, but that of John the Baptist, and include the two brief episodes of the presentation in the

CHRIST'S BAPTISM, HIS TRANSFIGURATION, HIS DEATH AND HIS RESURRECTION

The voice from the cloud proclaiming 'This is my Son', first heard at Jesus' baptism, is heard again at the Transfiguration. But notice how the Transfiguration is set between two sort of bookends, where Jesus tells the disciples that he must suffer, die, and rise again:

Jesus began to make it clear to his disciples that he was destined to go to Jerusalem and suffer grievously at the hands of the elders and chief priests and scribes, to be put to death and to be raised up on the third day . . .

Six days later, Jesus took with him Peter and James and his brother John, and led them up a high mountain where they could be alone. There in their presence he was transfigured . . . Suddenly a bright cloud covered them with shadow, and from the cloud there came a voice which said, 'This is my Son, the Beloved; he enjoys my favour. Listen to him . . .'

One day, when they were going through Galilee, Jesus said to them, 'The Son of Man is going to be handed over into the power of men; they will put him to death, and on the third day he will be raised to life again.'

Matthew 16:21-17:23
The pattern presented here from Matthew's Gospel
- *first prophecy of the passion and resurrection*
- *the Transfiguration, with its echoes of Jesus' baptism*
- *the second prophecy of the passion*
has exact parallels in Mark 8:27-9:32 and in Luke 9:22-45.

temple and the three days when the 12-year-old Jesus is 'lost' in the temple. Mark has no such introductory chapter, but launches us straight into the teaching of John the Baptist.

Clearly, what is important for the Gospels is not the private, hidden life of Jesus. Yes, space is given to the human birth of Jesus – but the fact that it is missing in two Gospels and given minimal coverage in the other two shows that it has only relative significance.

What interests the Gospels is the public life and ministry of Christ, and all four Gospels make Christ's baptism the starting point of that ministry.

Let us make no mistake, we are *not* talking here about Christian baptism. Being plunged in water as a purification rite and as a symbol of changing one's life for the better is not a Christian invention! John the Baptist was using a symbolic rite that was already familiar.

Jesus – the very one who has no need of purification – accepts to undergo such a rite, and God uses the rite to affirm who Jesus is:

As soon as Jesus was baptised
he came up from the water,
and suddenly the heavens opened
and he saw the Spirit of God
descending like a dove
and coming to rest on him.
And a voice spoke from heaven,
'This is my son, the beloved,
my favour rests on him.'
(Matthew 3:16-17)

There are exact parallels in Mark 1:9-11 and Luke 3:21-22.

In John's Gospel, John the Baptist declares:
I saw the Spirit coming down on him
from heaven like a dove
and sitting on him. . . .
I am the witness that he is the Chosen
One of God.
(John 1:32, 34)

So, all four Gospels tell us that the baptism of Jesus implies:
- the coming of the Spirit upon him and that the Spirit 'rests' on him

- that in baptism God (expressed as 'a voice from heaven') says 'this is my son', or 'my chosen one'.

For the Gospels, Jesus' life as the Christ starts symbolically at his baptism: this baptism is the sign that the Spirit is with him and that he is the Son of God. The Gospels want us to see that is why we too, choose to be baptised: in order that the Spirit may come and rest upon us, and so that we too may be recognised by God as his sons and daughters.

Jesus is baptised only once, so we might expect this to be the last mention of baptism in the Gospels. We would be wrong, because Jesus speaks several other times of his 'baptism' – not in the past tense as something that is already past and over, but as something that is in the future.

There is the moment when apostles James and John are seeking the best place in heaven. Jesus asks them if they know what they are asking for!

Can you drink the cup that I must
drink
or be baptised with the baptism
with which I must be baptised?
(Mark 10:38-39)

Here Jesus is not talking about being submerged in water, but being submerged in death. It is no accident that these same two apostles, James and John will be witnesses to the transfiguration, and that they will hear the same voice from heaven saying again, 'This is my Son ...' In what we call the Transfiguration, they are offered a glimpse of Christ in glory, in which those who pass through baptism also share. However, in the Gospels, Christ's transfiguration is inextricably linked to his forthcoming passion and death (see margin column left).

James and John will also be in the Garden of Gethsemane with Jesus, at the moment the 'baptism' of which he spoke begins. At that point, they seem incapable of sharing it with him, unable to stay awake and be with him. However, tradition tells us that James proved he could share that baptism, since he was the first apostle to be martyred (just before Easter, under the persecution of

Herod Agrippa I, in either AD 43 or 44).

In John's Gospel, the baptism of Jesus is followed by the wedding at Cana (where water plays a key role), the cleansing of the Temple (to be destroyed and raised 'in three days'), and then Nicodemus comes to Jesus ('by night', John adds symbolically). Jesus tells him:

> Unless a man is born from above
> he cannot see the kingdom of God.

Nicodemus takes Jesus literally, and asks 'How can a grown man be born? Can he go back into his mother's womb and be born again?' Jesus replies:

> I tell you most solemnly,
> unless a man is born through water
>   and the Spirit,
> he cannot enter the kingdom of God;
> what is born of flesh is flesh,
> what is born of the Spirit is Spirit.
> Do not be surprised when I say:
> You must be born from above.
> The wind blows wherever it pleases;
> you hear its sound,
> but you cannot tell where it comes from
>   or where it is going.
> That is how it is with all who are born
>   of the Spirit.
> (John 3:3-8)

The next time Nicodemus appears in the Gospel it is to anoint ('to christ' – see chapter on confirmation, page 34) the body of the dead Jesus before it is placed in the tomb (cf. John 19:38-39).

Immediately before this, John has told us how Pilate sent soldiers to ensure that Jesus and the other two crucified with him were dead. The conventional way to do this was to break their legs …

> When they came to Jesus,
> they found he was already dead,
> and so instead of breaking his legs
> one of the soldiers pierced his side with
>   a lance;
> and immediately there came out blood
>   and water.
> (John 19:33-34)

Here is where baptism and the Eucharist draw their sense and their power: from the saving death of Christ.

> **See where you are baptised,**
> **see where baptism comes from;**
> **from the cross of Christ,**
> **from his death.**
> **There is the whole mystery:**
> **he died for you.**
> **In him you are redeemed,**
> **in him you are saved.**
> **Saint Ambrose,**
> *De Sacramentis 2, 6*

To sum up, whenever the Gospels mention baptism before Christ's death and resurrection, then, it is to make clear the meaning of baptism:

– it implies the coming of the Spirit

– it means we become children of God, like Christ

– it is being born again, as children of God, to life in the Spirit

– it implies joining Christ, and passing with him through death with the promise of rising with him, because Jesus speaks of his passion and death as his 'baptism'.

Whenever baptism is mentioned by Jesus after the resurrection, it takes the form of a command.

In Matthew's Gospel, Christ's very last words to the eleven apostles are:

> All authority in heaven and on earth
> has been given to me.
> Go therefore, make disciples of all
>   nations;
> baptise them
> in the name of the Father and of the
>   Son and of the Holy Spirit
> and teach them to observe all the
>   commands I gave you.
> And know that I am with you always;
> yes to the end of time.
> (Matthew 28:18-20)

Mark – true to character – expresses the same more concisely:

> Go out to the whole world;
> proclaim the Good News to all
>   creation.
> He who believes and is baptised will
>   be saved.
> (Mark 16:16)

There are several key ideas that we can summarise here:

– Christ himself gives the Apostles the command to baptise

– baptism is offered to all ('all nations'; 'all creation')

– baptism implies living according to Christ's teaching and bearing witness to him

– baptism implies the presence of Christ with us 'to the end of time'

– baptism implies faith (Mark), faith in the Trinity (Matthew).

BAPTISM IN THE CHURCH OF THE NEW TESTAMENT

Luke makes no explicit mention in his gospel account of the ascension of the command to baptise. But in Luke's account of the ascension in the Acts of the Apostles, Jesus speaks about a baptism that the apostles are still to receive:

Wait here for what the Father promised.
John baptised with water
but you will be baptised with the Holy Spirit …
You will receive power
when the Holy Spirit comes upon you,
and then you will be my witnesses to the ends of the earth.
(Acts 1:4-8)

Again, we have the explicit ideas that

– baptism is for all 'to the ends of the earth'

– baptism is to do with witnessing to Christ.

The promise of Acts 1 is fulfilled in Acts 2, at Pentecost. The apostles are well and truly baptised by the Holy Spirit, and inspired to fulfil Christ's command. They start to preach, and the essence of Peter's first sermon is the paschal mystery, the mystery of Christ's death, resurrection and glorification (Acts 2:14-36). Moved by this teaching, the crowd asks, 'What must we do?' Peter replies:

You must repent
and every one of you must be baptised
in the name of Jesus Christ
for the forgiveness of your sins
and you will receive the gift of the Holy Spirit.
(Acts 2:38-40)

Luke adds that the crowd 'accepted what Peter said and were baptised. That very day about 3,000 were added to their number.' (Acts 2:41)

Faithful to Christ's command the apostles (and their collaborators, the deacons – see page 125) offer baptism 'to all nations':

to Jews	Acts 2:41
to Samaritans	Acts 8:12-13
and to Gentiles	Acts 18:8 (Corinth), 19:1-7 (Ephesus)

In the Acts of the Apostles we also see that, in fidelity to the mission Christ entrusted, baptism always implies the gift of faith, and the purpose of faith and baptism is salvation. The episode where Paul and Silas are in prison illustrates this well. When the prison doors are miraculously opened, and their chains fall off, the gaoler asks 'What must I do to be saved?' Perhaps he had a more material sense of being saved in mind; but what Paul and Silas offer is eternal salvation:

Become a believer in the Lord Jesus, and you will be saved.

Luke continues the narrative: 'Then they preached the word of the Lord to him and all his family. Late as it was, he took them to wash their wounds and was baptised then and there with all his household.' (Acts 16:31-33)

For Paul, baptism is our personal sharing in the death of Christ so as to rise with him:

You have been buried with him,
when you were baptised;
and by baptism, too,
you have been raised up with him
through your belief in the power of God
who raised him from the dead.
(Colossians 2:12)

We have already seen this paschal truth expressed in Romans 6 (see page 15) – a text which is the final reading before the Gospel at the Paschal Vigil on Easter Saturday night.

For the apostolic Church, it is clear that this incorporation into Christ which baptism implies takes place through joining the body of Christ which is the Church.

> *We were baptised*
> *into one body*
> *in a single Spirit,*
> *Jews as well as Greeks,*
> *slaves as well as free men,*
> *and we were all given*
> *the same Spirit to drink*
>
> *(1 Corinthians 12:13)*

BAPTISM IN THE EARLY CENTURIES

In the early days of the Church the water rite of baptism was part of a much fuller rite of initiation, associated with the laying on of hands, anointings, and the sharing for the first time at the eucharistic table. In other words, Christian initiation was celebrated in a continuous rite involving what we would now call the sacraments of baptism-confirmation-Eucharist.

To mark solemnly and clearly the meaning of initiation as incorporation into the death, resurrection and glorification of Christ, this final great rite was celebrated during the Easter Vigil. This was the Church's major feast, the night when new children for the Church were born through birth to new life in baptism.

This vision of 'new life' certainly did look forward to life with Christ after resurrection, but it also meant beginning to live life in Christ here and now, before death. Becoming a Christian implied a radical commitment to live a Christian life, utterly different from the standards of the surrounding pagan world. The Church, therefore, took great care to offer the candidates a very long period of preparation, both for their sake and for that of the Church. Each candidate needed to know what was expected, and whether he or she was capable of the demands of the Christian life. The Church knew full well that baptism – while being a gift – brought considerable responsibilities, and needed to be sure there was a reasonable chance that these would be fulfilled. For example, there were certain professions and activities that were considered incompatible with being a Christian: being in the Roman army (because soldiers had to swear an oath of loyalty to the Emperor as god); the theatre (because it presented principally the myths of classical gods and goddesses).

With Christ as the Way, initiation represented the first stages of a journey, covered at a pace that corresponded to the nature and capacities of the candidate. On average the whole process from first interest to being baptised-confirmed and receiving the Eucharist for the first time lasted something like three years. Within this journey, there were certain clear stages, each of which was marked by certain symbolic rites.

The first stage was the straightforward interest that a non-believer expressed, a healthy curiosity, wanting to know more about Christ, about the Church and Christian life. Such people were called *enquirers*, and over a period of time, their questions would be answered, they would be led from simple curiosity to a longing to be joined to Christ. As soon as it was clear to both the Church and the individual that there was such a genuine thirst, they were formally welcomed by the bishop and the community in a *rite of entry into the catechumenate*.

The second stage, then, was the *catechumenate*, and the candidates were called *catechumens*. The rite of entry into the catechumenate had a double function. First of all, the local community formally acknowledged these new fellow-travellers – who now therefore had the right to call themselves 'Christians', and assured them of their support. The rite also served as a reminder to the community of their duty to support and lead the catechumens on by their prayer and their example. In the catechumenate, the preparation of the catechumens became more systematic. They had a special place within the Sunday assembly. They took part in the Sunday liturgy of the Word and listened to the bishop's explanation of what the readings meant. However, they were not yet allowed to participate at the Eucharist, and were formally dismissed after the homily. The Creed – the profession of faith which they had not yet made – was the distinguishing feature between those who were baptised (known as the 'faithful') and those who were catechumens.

BAPTISM IN THE EARLY CHURCH

HIPPOLYTUS
(Early-third-century, Rome)

Hippolytus offers a description of one single celebration of initiation, which encompassed baptism, confirmation and first sharing in the Eucharist (see the account of the anointing with chrism from this same source in the chapter on confirmation, page 41). Notice how the threefold profession of faith is linked with a threefold immersion.

Those who are to be baptised take off their clothes. The little children are baptised first: if they can answer for themselves, let them do so; but if they cannot, let their parents or someone else from the family answer.

Then the men are baptised; and finally, the women are baptised.

The presbyter takes hold of each candidate who is to be baptised and asks the candidate to say, 'I renounce you, Satan, and all your service and all your works.' When the candidate has said this, the presbyter anoints him with the oil of exorcism saying, 'Let all evil spirits depart far from you.'

The candidate then goes over to the presbyter who is standing at the side of the water for baptism. The candidates stand in the water, naked, accompanied by a deacon. When the person who is to be baptised goes down into the water, the one who baptises lays his hand on him and says, 'Do you believe in God the almighty Father?' And the candidate is to say, 'I believe'. And he is immediately immersed for the first time.

Then this question is asked, 'Do you believe in Christ Jesus, the Son of God, who was born of the Holy Spirit and the Virgin Mary, was crucified in the days of Pontius Pilate, died and was buried and rose the third day, alive from the dead and ascended into the heavens and took his seat at the right hand of the Father and will come to judge the living and the dead?'
When the candidate replies 'I believe', he is immersed a second time.
And again, 'Do you believe in the Holy Spirit in the Holy Church, and the resurrection of the flesh?'
The candidate is to say, 'I believe', and so he is immersed the third time...

(Apostolic Tradition 21-22)

BAPTISM IN THE EARLY CHURCH

CYRIL
(Early-fourth-century, Jerusalem)
What follows is taken from a sermon preached to the baptised after their baptism, inviting them to interpret the rites that they have undergone. What gives added weight to Cyril's word is the fact that the baptistery at Jerusalem was built over the presumed site of Christ's tomb. Imagine what it must have been like to hear Romans 6, about going down into the tomb with Christ, quoted in these circumstances!

Then you were led by the hand to the holy pool of sacred baptism, just as Christ was taken from the cross to the nearby sepulchre. Each person was asked if he believed in the name of the Father and of the Son and of the Holy Spirit. You made the confession that brings salvation, you were submerged three times in the water and emerged. By this symbolic gesture you were re-enacting in a secret way the burial of Christ for three days in the tomb…

In one and the same action you died and were born; the water of salvation was for you both tomb and mother. In a single moment you both die and are born, and your being born was simultaneous with your death.

How strange! How astonishing! We did not really die, we were not really buried, we did not really hang from a cross and rise again. We imitated it in symbol, but our salvation is real…This is why, as we have heard just now, Paul acclaim,* 'Do you not know that all of us who have been baptised in Christ Jesus, it is into his death that we were baptised? … If we have been planted together with him in a death like his death, we shall certainly be planted together with him in a resurrection like his.' How appropriate that Paul says* 'planted together': just as 'the true vine'** was planted here in Jerusalem, we have been planted with him by sharing in the baptism of his death …

(Sermon 2)

*Clear references to Romans 6: notice how the second quote plays on the interpretation of 'neophytes' as being newly planted.

** John 15

Whenever the catechumens were judged ready for baptism, they would be formally called by the bishop, in the name of the Church, in *the rite of election*. The catechumens had now become the *elect*.

This third stage was called the period of enlightenment. What we now know as the season of Lent grew out of this time of intense preparation of the candidates and the community for their celebration together of initiation at the Easter Vigil. So, for example, we find the three great Sundays of Lent are set in place, which gently explore, through the magnificent episodes from John's Gospel, the various symbolic elements the elect would encounter in that celebration:

water	hence the Gospel of the Samaritan woman (John 4:5-42)
the candle	hence the Gospel of the man born blind (John 9:1-41)
white garment	hence the Gospel of Lazarus, emerging from the tomb in his shroud (John 11:1-45)

The practical elements of the rite were not explained to the elect in advance: there was a great confidence that these powerful rites would speak for themselves. These Gospels served to feed the whole assembly's reflection on the significance of these rites. On closer examination, these Gospels also shed light on the various preparatory rites that took place during these last weeks before the paschal vigil.

There was a sort of public testing of the candidates' preparedness for initiation at the forthcoming Easter Vigil. These were called the 'scrutinies'.

In the early centuries, there was a very keen sense of the presence of evil and evil forces. Part of the support that the Church offered was a series of intense prayers known as 'exorcisms'. The basic idea was that in order to be filled with the Holy Spirit, the candidates should first be emptied of every harmful or evil spirit.

This was also the time when the elect were initiated into the two great baptismal texts. They were entrusted, for the first time, with the Creed, and then with the

Our Father. This entrusting took place in a rite known as the *presentation*, or in Latin the *tradition*.

The enlightenment reached its climax on Holy Saturday night, when the candidates took part in the great vigil of prayers and readings which began at dusk and continued all through the night. As dawn was breaking, the candidates would be led to the baptistery, for the triple immersion in the name of the Trinity. Rising from the font, they were enveloped in white, given the lighted candle, and led back to join the main assembly, where they were welcomed by the whole community. The bishop then laid hands on them, anointed them, and gave them the kiss of peace. The Eucharist then began, in which the newly baptised took part and received communion for the first time.

Those who passed through the rite of initiation became full members of the Church – but their journey on the Way who is Christ continued. To signify this, and to help them make this transition, there was another and final stage, which lasted throughout the whole of Easter, until Pentecost. This was the period of *mystagogy*: now, through the eyes of faith, guided by the bishop, they explored the mysteries they had undergone and sought to understand them, so as to live them out.

The term given to the freshly initiated was *neophytes*, which can be translated as 'converts', or as 'new beings', or as 'new plants'. They were like new seedlings, freshly planted, needing the mystagogy, this time of special care and attention, to ensure that their roots were solid:

Your new birth
was not from any mortal seed
but from the everlasting word
of the living and eternal God
(1 Peter 1:23)

FOURTH CENTURY ONWARDS

The conversion of the Roman Emperor Constantine and his making Christianity the state religion had repercussions for all the sacraments – not least the way Christian initiation was celebrated.

One major change which begins at this time – and which is fully explored in the chapter on confirmation (see pages 33-37) – is the gradual separation of the sacraments of baptism and confirmation into two distinct liturgical celebrations.

Clearly, the lengthy process from catechumenate to mystagogy was designed for adults – although we do know that children were baptised with their parents.

With the end of persecutions against the Church and a greater harmony between Christian life and everyday life as a citizen, many of the things that once would have caused greatest obstacles to and difficulties in living as a Christian were gone. The rites, with their potent symbolism remained, but the necessity for such a demanding preparation became less urgent.

Increasingly, it became standard practice to baptise children and babies. By the time we reach the twelfth century and the theological reflections of the Scholastics on baptism, the custom of baptising babies 'as soon as possible' had become standard practice.

Curiously, despite this radical change in the circumstances of the candidate, the structure of the rite remained the same: the many preliminary rites, once celebrated at different times, were all squeezed into one ceremony. Throughout the priest addressed the candidate himself or herself, although the responses were made by the godparents.

The Second Vatican Council demanded a twofold revision of the sacrament of baptism. Its first demand was that:

> *The catechumenate for adults, comprising several distinct steps, is to be restored and to be put into use … By this means the period of the catechumenate, which is intended as a time of suitable instruction, may be sanctified by sacred rites to be celebrated at successive intervals.*
> (Sacrosanctum Concilium 64)

The council's second demand was that the rite be appropriately adapted when the candidate is a baby or a child too young to answer for themselves.

BAPTISM TODAY
1. Christian initiation of adults

The requests made by the Second Vatican Council have both been fulfilled: in 1972, the official Latin edition of the Rite of Christian Initiation was promulgated, and after something like 1,600 years of disuse, the full catechumenical process was restored. The English edition (which is not just a simple translation, but translation, presentation and arrangement designed to suit the culture and customs of the English-speaking world) was published in 1987, and has been standard practice since Advent 1988.

This Rite completely restores the four periods of:

– **evangelisation and precatechumenate** (stage 1)

> *This period of precatechumenate is of great importance … It is a time of evangelisation: faithfully and constantly the living Lord is proclaimed and Jesus Christ whom he has sent for the salvation of all. Thus those who are not yet Christians, their hearts opened by the Holy Spirit, may believe and be freely converted to the Lord and commit themselves sincerely to him …*
> (RCIA 36)

– **catechumenate**, which may last several years (stage 2)

> *… an extended period during which the candidates are given suitable pastoral formation and guidance, aimed at training them in the Christian life … This is achieved in four ways:*
>
> *1. A suitable catechesis … gradual and complete, solidly supported by celebrations of the Word. This catechesis leads the candidates not only to an appropriate acquaintance with dogmas and precepts but also to a profound sense of the mystery of salvation …*
>
> *2. … the catechumens learn to turn more readily to God in prayer, to bear witness to the faith, in all things to keep their hopes set on Christ, to follow supernatural*

AMBROSE
(Late-fourth-century, Milan)

The same threefold immersion, and its symbolism of going down into death and burial with Christ, are explicitly evoked by Ambrose.

You were asked, 'Do you believe in God the Father Almighty?' You replied, 'I believe', and you were immersed.

You were asked a second time, 'Do you believe in our Lord Jesus Christ and in his cross?' You replied 'I believe', and you were immersed – which means that you were buried with Christ. For the one who is buried with Christ rises again with Christ.

You were asked a third time, 'Do you believe also in the Holy Spirit?' You replied, 'I believe', and you were immersed a third time, so that the threefold confession might absolve the numerous lapses of the past…

Do not be surprised that we are baptised in one name, that is, in the name of the Father and of the Son and of the Holy Spirit…

The apostle exclaims, as you have just heard in the reading,* 'Whoever is baptised, is baptised in the death of Jesus.' What does 'in the death' mean? It means that just as Christ died, so you will taste death; that just as Christ died to sin and lives to God, so through the sacrament of baptism you are dead to the old enticements of sin and have risen again through the grace of Christ. This is a death, then, not in the reality of bodily death, but in likeness. When you are immersed, you receive the likeness of death and burial, you receive the sacrament of the cross . . .

(De Sacramentis)

*As in Cyril of Jerusalem, (see opposite) again a clear reference to Romans 6 (see page 15).

inspiration in their deeds, and to practise love of neighbour …

3. *The Church, like a mother, helps the catechumens on their journey by means of suitable liturgical rites, which purify the catechumens little by little and strengthen them with God's blessing …*

4. *… catechumens should also learn how to work actively with others to spread the Gospel and build up the Church by witness of their lives and by professing their faith.*
(RCIA 75)

– **period of purification and enlightenment**, which normally coincides with Lent (stage 3)

… for both the elect and the local community … a time for spiritual recollection in preparation for the celebration of the paschal mystery … This is a period of more intense spiritual preparation … intended to purify the minds and hearts of the elect as they search their own consciences and do penance.
(RCIA 125-6)

This process of purification and enlightenment is brought about, in particular, by:

• **the scrutinies**, which are rites

for soul-searching and repentance. They are designed 'to uncover, then heal, all that is weak, defective, or sinful in the hearts of the elect; to bring out, then strengthen all that is upright, strong and good …'
(RCIA 128)

• **the presentations**, where

the Church lovingly entrusts the Creed and the Lord's Prayer, the ancient texts that have always been regarded as expressing the heart of the Church's faith and prayer.
(RCIA 134)

– **mystagogy**, or post-baptismal catechesis (stage 4);

this is a time for the community and the neophytes together to grow in deepening their grasp of the paschal mystery and in making it part of their lives through meditation on

the Gospel, sharing in the Eucharist, and doing the works of charity.
(RCIA 234)

and the three steps which mark the transition from one stage to another:

• **acceptance as a catechumen** (from stage 1 to stage 2)

Assembling publicly for the first time, the candidates declare their intention to the Church and the Church in turn, carrying out its apostolic mission, accepts them as persons who intend to become members …
(RCIA 41)

• **rite of election** (from stage 2 to stage 3)

… on the basis of the testimony of godparents and catechists and of the catechumens' reaffirmation of their intention, the Church judges their state of readiness and decides on their advancement toward the sacraments of initiation. Thus the Church makes its 'election', … so called because acceptance by the Church is founded on the election by God, in whose name the Church acts.'
(RCIA 106)

• **celebration of the sacraments of initiation, baptism, confirmation and Eucharist** (from stage 3 to stage 4)

Through this final step, the elect, receiving pardon for their sins, are admitted into the people of God. They are graced with adoption as children of God and are led by the Holy Spirit into the promised fullness of time begun in Christ and, as they share in the eucharistic sacrifice and meal, even to a foretaste of the kingdom of heaven.
(RCIA 198)

This is a magnificent programme which, in the decade or so it has been in practice, has been revitalising the life of the local community. By the constant interplay, both within and outside the liturgy, between those who are en route to the sacraments and those who are already full members, the local church can become a more dynamic, more vibrant sacrament of the Church, making

Christ's growing body present and active in this world, working toward the building up of his kingdom and its values.

2. Baptism of infants

Our historical exploration has shown that the Church has always baptised infants – even if in the very early times, this was by exception rather than standard practice. In the Acts of the Apostles, we are told that complete 'households' received baptism, which may have included infants. Certainly, there is explicit evidence that infants were baptised from the second century onwards.

Even if, for infants, the sacrament of baptism is celebrated separately from the other sacraments of initiation, and the pre-baptismal rites are presented in a very abridged way, it remains no less true that becoming a Christian means setting out on a journey, on the Way that is Christ. For the baby, the post-baptismal stage will be long, as he or she grows and perfects the initiation begun in baptism by being confirmed and making first communion. The obligation that falls more personally on adult candidates in the pre-baptismal stages falls on the parents in the case of the baptism of a baby. Indeed, current Canon Law sees the two as parallel: Canon 851 has a first paragraph concerning adult candidates, and then a second, which says:

> *The parents of a child who is to be baptised, and those who are to undertake the office of sponsors, are to be suitably instructed on the meaning of this sacrament and the obligations attaching to it. The parish priest is to see to it that either he or others duly prepare the parents, by means of pastoral advice and indeed by prayer together; a number of families might be brought together for this purpose and, where possible, each family visited.*

(Code of Canon Law, Canon 851)

In terms of the evolution of theology, the fact that babies were baptised led to the development of the idea of 'original sin'. Baptism is the sacrament of conversion: conversion *to* Christ, but *away* from sin.

What sin could a baby have committed? None, most evidently; therefore the forgiveness in baptism has to be understood as converting something altogether more radical: our fatally flawed human nature (see quote from *Catechism,* right).

This is why the church demands that babies of Christian parents be baptised as soon as possible (see Canon Law in the margin column on page 24). As a sacrament, baptism speaks to us of the nature of God: in the baptism of infants we see more clearly the utter gratuitousness of the salvation that God offers: it is a grace and gift of God that does not presuppose any human merit.

Through baptism, the baby becomes a member of Christ, which is effected by being incorporated into the Church. Even if the baby may not appreciate it at the time, it makes far more sense for the baptism to take place during the Sunday celebration of Mass, so that the assembly can welcome this new member to the body of Christ. In which case, the Liturgy of Baptism will follow the Liturgy of the Word, immediately after the homily; after the three post-baptismal rites, the Eucharistic celebration continues with the Prayer of the Faithful, with special mention being made of the Church's new member, and the parents and godparents.

Whether the rite is celebrated within Mass or outside of Mass, the ritual expects that it will involve movement. The baptism of a baby squeezes a whole series of gestures and symbols into one single ceremony. The great symbolic metaphor that underlies baptism is that of setting out on the journey into Christ who is the Way. Especially when the rite is 'simplified' into a single celebration, this sense of journey must be conveyed by the processions that take place from outside the church building to inside, and again from place to place within the church.

BAPTISM OF CHILDREN

The Rite of Baptism of Children

From the earliest times, the Church, to which the mission of preaching the Gospel and of baptism was entrusted, has baptised not only adults but children as well.

Our Lord said 'Unless a man is reborn in water and the Holy Spirit, he cannot enter the kingdom of God.' The Church has always understood these words to mean that children should not be deprived of baptism, because they are baptised in the faith of the Church, a faith proclaimed for them by their parents and godparents, who represent both the local Church and the whole society of saints and believers. 'The whole Church is the mother of all and the mother of each.'
(Rite of Baptism for Children, Intro 2)

The Catechism

Born with a fallen human nature and tainted by original sin, children also have need of the new birth in Baptism to be freed from the power of darkness and brought into the realm of the freedom of the children of God, to which all are called [cf. Cor 1:12-14]. The sheer gratuitousness of the grace of salvation is particularly manifest in infant baptism. The Church and the parents would deny a child the priceless grace of becoming a child of God were they not to confer baptism shortly after birth [see Canon 867, quoted below].

Christian parents will recognise that this practice also accords with their role as nurturers of the life that God has entrusted to them [cf. LG 11; 41; GS 48; Canon 868].

The practice of infant baptism is an immemorial tradition of the Church. There is explicit testimony to this practice from the second century on, and it is quite possible that, from the beginning of the

**BAPTISM
OF CHILDREN
(continued)**

apostolic preaching, when whole 'households' received baptism, infants may also have been baptised [cf. Acts 16:15, 33, 18:8, 1 Cor 1:16].
(Catechism 1250-1252)

The Code of Canon Law

§1 Parents are obliged to see that their infants are baptised within the first few weeks. As soon as possible after the birth, indeed even before it, they are to approach the parish priest to ask for the sacrament for their child, and to be themselves duly prepared for it.

§2 If the infant is in danger of death, it is to be baptised without any delay.

(Canon 867)

OUTLINE

Here is an outline of the Rite of Baptism of infants:

INTRODUCTORY RITES
Reception and signing with the sign of the cross

LITURGY OF THE WORD
Reading
Response
Gospel
Homily
Prayer of the Faithful

LITURGY OF BAPTISM
Exorcism
Anointing with the oil of catechumens
Blessing of or thanksgiving over the
    baptismal water
Baptismal promises
Baptism
Anointing with chrism
Presentation of the lighted candle
Presentation of the white garment
[The Ephphatha rite]

CONCLUDING RITE
The Lord's Prayer
Blessings

INTRODUCTORY RITES
Reception and signing with the cross

The parents and the godparents wait with the candidate for the baptism at the door of the church. If it is warm enough, they might wait outside, so that the symbolism of being invited in by the priest in the name of the community is more evident. If it is during the Sunday Eucharist, so that the congregation can share in this rite, the candidate, parents and godparents should be just inside the entrance.

The Ritual offers the celebrant considerable freedom in receiving the candidate: the presumption is that he will know how to welcome this baby in a warm and personal way. Such a welcome will express better the spiritual welcome that the Church offers.

The celebrant asks the parents the name they have chosen for the baby. This is not just out of personal interest, or for the purely practical reason that he needs to know to use the name later at the moment

of baptism. Names are highly symbolic, they are the means by which we identify ourselves to others. In a way, having a personal name is a declaration of each individual's uniqueness. In asking the name, the Church is recognising that this uniqueness, the personality of this baby is a gift of God. Each one of us is made by God, known by God, and loved by him as we are for what we are:

*Now thus says the Lord
who created you:
do not be afraid,
    for I have redeemed you;
have called you by your name,
    you are mine.*
(Isaiah 43:1)

Customarily, the baby is given the name of a saint: the litany of the saints, solemnly prayed at the Easter Vigil for adult candidates, is used later in a shortened form for infant baptism. The giving of a saint's name serves as a symbol that the Church into which the baby is being welcomed transcends here and now, and includes all who ever were and ever will be baptised. Today, this candidate is being welcomed into 'the communion of saints'.

The priest then asks the parents and godparents what it is that they – on behalf of the baby – wish from the Church. The fact that the ritual gives no fixed answer shows that this is something which the parents and godparents, in discussion with the parish, should have thought about, have discussed, and come to a decision. That decision they now make in this public request for 'faith' or 'baptism' or 'entrance into the Church'.

Baptism is certainly a freely offered gift of God, and grants certain privileges, but it brings with it certain responsibilities. The priest sums these up, and asks if the parents are ready to assume them:

*You have asked to have your child
    baptised.
In doing so you are accepting the
    responsibility
of training him/her in the practice of
    the faith.
It will be your duty to bring him/her
    up
to keep God's commandments
as Christ taught us,
by loving God and your neighbour.*

The parents are not alone. The role of the godparents is to help, which they now promise to do, in response to the priest's question of them.

Assured by their replies, the priest welcomes the child, speaking to the child directly and personally, in the name of the community, which represents the Church:

> …[candidate's name],
> the Christian community welcomes
>   you with great joy.
> In its name I claim you for Christ
> by the sign of the cross.
> I now trace the cross on your forehead
> and invite your parents and godparents
>   to do the same.

One of the original meanings of 'sacrament', before it was used by the Church, was to mean the branding of Roman legionaries to show that they belonged to the army (see introductory chapter, page 8). The child is now marked with the 'sacrament' of his or her belonging:

> The sign of the cross
> marks with the imprint of Christ
> the one who is going to belong to him
> and signifies the grace of redemption
> won for us by his cross.
> (Catechism 1235)

Here is where movement can be symbolic: from their original position at the door of the church, the candidate and those who accompany him or her are now led to their places among the assembly, to share in the Liturgy of the Word.

LITURGY OF THE WORD

We have explored the importance that scripture has in the process of adult initiation: years of sharing in the Liturgy of the Word, hearing scripture proclaimed and explained. The texts read and explained at the baby's baptism may not mean much to him or her on that day – but they are as much for the parents, godparents and the others present at the ceremony. Baptism is about faith, and faith is stirred and kept alive by the Word of God. Faith is answering the call of God – a call heard in a privileged way in the proclamation of the scriptures, especially the Gospel (see right-hand margin column).

There are two very ancient forms of prayer of supplication in the tradition of the Church: the Prayer of the Faithful and the Litany of the Saints. The ritual allows considerable flexibility in how the community now prays, as Church, for its needs, with a special thought for the candidate, the family and the godparents. A shortened form of the litany is proposed, to which particular intentions can be added.

LITURGY OF BAPTISM
Exorcism and anointing with the oil of catechumens

'Exorcism' may conjure up all kinds of images: in fact, it is simply a technical word for a solemn prayer for liberation from sin. A useful analogy may be that of having the baby inoculated against various life-threatening diseases. Here the Church invokes the power of God against what could threaten the candidate's spiritual life. As we discovered in our exploration of the history of Christian initiation, exorcism should not be considered on its own: it is a preparatory rite, an emptying, but only so as the better to be filled by the Holy Spirit:

> Almighty and ever-living God,
> you sent your only Son into the world
> to cast out the power of Satan, spirit of
>   evil,
> to rescue humankind from the
>   kingdom of darkness,
> and bring them into the splendour of
>   your kingdom of light.
> We pray for this child:
> set him/her free from original sin,
> make him/her a temple of your glory,
> and send your Holy Spirit to dwell
>   with him/her.

This is a prayer about freedom, about being released from the slavery of sin:

> When Christ freed us,
> he meant us to remain free.
> Stand firm, then,
> and do not submit again to the yoke of
>   slavery.
> (Galatians 3:1)

As a sign of the 'firmness' that the Christian life demands, the baby is anointed with the oil of catechumens, while the accompanying prayer invokes the strength of Christ:

> *We anoint you with the oil of salvation in the name of Christ our Saviour: may he strengthen you with his power.*

Blessing of or thanksgiving over the baptismal water

This is another moment that can be heightened by a procession. If the church has a font, the candidate is now led there by the priest, together with the parents and godparents. If the baptistery is hidden in a corner of the building, it would be preferable to set up a temporary font where it can be seen by all who are taking part in the celebration. It should, if possible, be sufficiently distinct in place from the ambo (the place for the readings) and the altar (the place for the Eucharist).

The prayer for the blessing of the water is one of the Church's oldest prayers. This prayer is, in itself, a magnificent commentary on the saving symbolism of water. Indeed, the *Catechism* (cf. Catechism, Nos. 1217-1225) uses this prayer as its way of explaining the meaning of baptism, both as prefigured in the Old Testament and as presented in the New:

– the waters of creation, over which the Spirit of God hovers and which thereby become the source of life

– the image of the flood, where water destroys evil, but where the just, Noah, is saved

– passing through the Red Sea means escape from slavery into freedom, escape from certain death

– the crossing of the Jordan which marks the end of the time in the desert and reaching the Promised Land

– Jesus' own baptism in the same River Jordan, where the Spirit descends and God recognises him as his Son

– the blood and water that flow from the side of Christ

– Christ's command to the apostles to make disciples of the whole world, baptising them …

> *Father,*
> *you give us grace through sacramental signs*
> *which tell us of the wonders of your unseen power.*
> *In baptism we use your gift of water*
> *which you have made a great symbol of the grace*
> *you give us in this sacrament.*
> *At the very dawn of creation*
> *your Spirit breathed on the waters,*
> *making them the well spring of all holiness.*
> *The waters of the great flood*
> *you made a sign of the waters of baptism*
> *that make an end of sin*
> *and a new beginning of goodness.*
> *Through the waters of the Red Sea*
> *you led Israel out of slavery*
> *to be an image of God's holy people,*
> *set free from sin by baptism.*
> *In the waters of the Jordan*
> *your Son was baptised by John*
> *and anointed with the Spirit.*
> *Your Son willed that water and blood should flow from his side*
> *as he hung upon the cross.*
> *After his resurrection he told his disciples:*
> *'Go out and teach all nations,*
> *baptising them in the name of the Father*
> *and of the Son and of the Holy Spirit.'*
> *Look now upon your Church*
> *and unseal for it the fountain of baptism.*
> *By the power of baptism*
> *give to the water of this font*
> *the grace of your Son.*

You created man in your likeness:
cleanse him from sin in a new birth to
*   innocence*
by water and the Spirit.

This great prayer is used at the Easter Vigil, so that if a baptism takes place during the Easter season it is not repeated, but one of two alternative prayers of thanksgiving is used. If the Church offers these, it is on the presumption that those who are present at the baptism have already been present at the Easter Vigil, hence the wish to avoid duplication. The alternatives are both centred on themes only from the New Testament, and both are Trinitarian. One focuses on the role of each Person of the Trinity in the overall plan of salvation; the other focuses on the sense of mission or call that baptism implies.

Baptismal promises

The baptismal promises are twofold: the renunciation of sin and the profession of faith. Baptism is about conversion, that means it is about turning away from something so as to turn to something else. In this double declaration, the candidate – or more exactly the parents and godparents on the baby's behalf – makes a personal public statement about dying to sin so as to live the new life of Christ. Those who make the promises on the baby's behalf are solemnly reminded of the serious duty that this implies:

Dear parents and godparents:
you have come here
to present this child for baptism.
By water and the Holy Spirit
he/she is to receive the gift of new life
from God who is love.
On your part,
you must make it your constant care
to bring him/her up in the practice of
*   the faith.*
See that the divine life which God
*   gives him/her*
is kept safe from the poison of sin,
to grow always stronger in his/her
*   heart.*

Traditionally there is a triple renunciation, made by declaring 'I do':

Do you reject sin,
so as to live in the freedom of God's
*   children?*

Do you reject the glamour of evil,
and refuse to be mastered by sin?
Do you reject Satan,
father of sin and prince of darkness?

which balances the threefold profession of faith:

Do you believe in God,
the Father almighty,
Creator of heaven and earth?
Do you believe in Jesus Christ, his only
*   Son, our Lord,*
who was born of the Virgin Mary,
was crucified, died and was buried,
rose from the dead?
Do you believe in the Holy Spirit,
the holy catholic Church,
the communion of saints,
the forgiveness of sins,
the resurrection of the body,
and life everlasting?

The celebrant acknowledges this solemn declaration and accepts it in the name of the Church, saying:

This is our faith.
This is the faith of the Church.
We are proud to profess it,
in Christ Jesus, our Lord.

Baptism

It is unambiguously clear that all the images employed in this ancient prayer involve being 'submerged' under the water: this, indeed, is the original meaning of the Greek verb to baptise. The essential meaning of baptism is better expressed by this idea of going down to death with Christ so as to come up, to rise with him.

The *Catechism* explains:

Baptism signifies and actually brings
*   about*
death to sin
and entry into the life
of the Most Holy Trinity
through configuration to the Paschal
*   Mystery of Christ.*
Baptism is performed in the most
*   expressive way*
by triple immersion in the baptismal
*   water.*
However, from ancient times
it has also been able to be conferred by
*   pouring the water*
three times over the candidate's head.
(Catechism 1239)

In the official books containing the rites, two ways of baptising are offered. The first – and the order is **not** accidental – is by immersion; the second is by the pouring of water.

> …[candidate's name]
> *I baptise you*
> *in the name of the Father*
> first immersion, or pouring
>
> *and of the Son*
> second immersion, or pouring
>
> *and of the Holy Spirit*
> third immersion or pouring.

The baptism is followed by three rites (plus a fourth optional rite) which express the immediate effects of baptism.

Anointing with chrism

The anointing with chrism signifies the gift of the Holy Spirit to the newly baptised, who has literally become 'a christ'; that is, 'one who is anointed by the Holy Spirit and incorporated into Jesus the Christ, priest, prophet and king.'

> *God the Father of our Lord Jesus*
>   *Christ,*
> *has freed you from sin,*
> *given you a new birth by water and*
>   *the Holy Spirit*
> *and welcomed you into his holy people.*
> *He now anoints you with the chrism*
>   *of salvation.*
> *As Christ was anointed Priest, Prophet*
>   *and King,*
> *so may you live always as a member of*
>   *his body,*
> *sharing everlasting life.*

Clothing with the white garment

The white garment is the visible sign of the newly baptised's dignity as a Christian.

> *… [newly-baptised's name],*
> *you have become a new creation*
> *and have clothed yourself in Christ.*
> *Receive this white garment*
> *and bring it unstained to the*
>   *judgement seat*
> *of our Lord Jesus Christ*
> *so that you may have everlasting life.*

Paul uses the eloquent metaphor of putting on a garment to express the new life found in Christ:

> *All baptised in Christ,*
> *you have clothed yourselves in Christ.*
> (Galatians 3:27)

Earlier in the same Letter Paul speaks not about putting on a garment, but of himself as being the garment, in which Christ lives:

> *I have been crucified with Christ*
> *and I live now*
> *not with my own life*
> *but with the life of Christ*
> *who lives in me.*
> (Galatians 2:20)

Presentation of the lighted candle

For adult candidates, the final climactic stage of their preparation is called 'enlightenment'. The newly baptised baby is offered a candle, lit from the Easter candle which represents the risen Christ in baptism; Christ has enlightened the baptised so that they, like him, may be the light of the world.

> *You have been enlightened by Christ.*
> *Walk always as children of the light*
> *and keep the flame of faith alive in*
>   *your hearts.*
> *When the Lord comes, may you go out*
>   *to meet him*
> *with all the saints in the heavenly*
>   *kingdom.*

> *You are the light of the world.*
> *A city built on a hill-top*
> *cannot be hidden.*
> *No one lights a lamp*
> *to hide it under a tub;*
> *they put it on the lamp-stand*
> *where it shines for every one*
> *in the house.*
> *In the same way*
> *your light must shine*
> *in the sight of all,*
> *so that, seeing your good works,*
> *they may give praise*
> *to your Father in heaven.*
> *(Matthew 5:14-16)*

[Ephphatha rite]

In the Rite of Christian Initiation of Adults, this symbolic gesture is performed as one of the final pre-baptismal rites. The sense is quite clear: the need of Christians to be open to hearing the word of God and to professing it.

This is an optional rite in infant baptism, and is performed now, after baptism, as recognition that while the baby cannot yet understand, in due course he or she must 'be open' (which is the literal translation of the Aramaic *'Ephphatha')*:

Ephphatha: that is, be opened,
that you may profess the faith you hear,
to the praise and glory of God.

CONCLUDING RITES

The Lord's Prayer

The baptismal rites around the font are now concluded. This is another moment for procession. As a baptised member of the Church, the baby is now symbolically brought to the altar. If baptism takes place during Mass, the newly-baptised, the parents and the godparents are led by the celebrant to their places for the Eucharist.

Even if Mass is not celebrated, the celebrant still leads them to the altar, where they stand for the prayers of the concluding rite.

Indeed, the introduction to the Lord's Prayer will explicitly evoke the two sacraments of initiation that await the newly baptised on his or her journey through the Christian life: confirmation and Eucharist, for which one day he or she will again stand at the altar.

Dearly beloved,
this child has been born again in
*   baptism.*
He/she is now called the child of God,
for so indeed he/she is.
In confirmation
he/she will receive
the fullness of God's Spirit.
In holy communion
he/she will share in the banquet of
*   Christ's sacrifice,*
calling God his/her Father in the midst
*   of the Church.*

The newly baptised, by incorporation into Christ, is a child of God, and therefore entitled to say the prayer of the children of God: 'Our Father …'

Blessings

By baptism, new children are born for the life of the Church. But these candidates for baptism are the fruit of the love of the mother and father, who provide in this way for the perpetuation of the people of God through the centuries (see *Lumen Gentium*, 11).

The Church honours the share in creation that God grants to parents by offering a blessing, first to the mother, then to the father:

Blessing for the mother

God the Father,
through his Son,
the Virgin Mary's child,
has brought joy to all Christian
*   mothers,*
as they see the hope of eternal life shine
*   on their children.*
May he bless the mother of this child.
She now thanks God for the gift of her
*   child.*
May she be with him or her for ever in
*   heaven,*
in Christ Jesus, our Lord.

Blessing for the father

God is the giver of all life, human and
*   divine.*
May he bless the father of this child.
He and his wife will be the first
*   teachers of their child*
in the ways of faith.
May they be also the best of teachers,
bearing witness to the faith
by what they say and do,
in Christ Jesus, our Lord.

CONFIRMATION
Sealed with the Gift of the Spirit

GIFTS AND TALENTS

Every one of us has gifts and talents:

- some are gifted with their hands and are good at craft work and practical things

- some have keen intellects, good concentration and sharp memories, which makes them good at study

- some have musical or other artistic gifts

- some are physically gifted, and so excel in sports and games

- some have the gift of an easy nature, excellent relationship skills, so they make good friends and helpers.

This list could easily be expanded, but what interests us is the fundamental truth behind any such list: everyone has some talent or gift.

Intriguingly, people who are handicapped in one way usually outshine so-called 'normal' people in other ways: the number of blind people who are extremely gifted at music, for example; the gentleness, the utter trust and the palpable spontaneous outgoing love of many who suffer from Down's syndrome.

For most people, the pattern is the same:

- we are born with an innate capacity for a certain talent

- we need to work at that natural gift to develop and improve it

- such development and improvement necessarily involves other people, who help in the process of training.

As Christians, we believe that our gifts and talents are God-given. They are given by God in love – and for love. That is to say, they are entrusted to us but for the benefit of all creation, for the good of others and not just ourselves. Our gifts are designed to make the world a better, a happier place. In other words, the privilege of our gifts brings with it the responsibility to develop them and use them as fully as possible, for our own good and that of others.

In thinking of gifts in this way, our talents are not so much about doing things, although admittedly, it is by doing that the gift is made visible to ourselves and to others. But the gift itself is deeper: it is not simply about doing, but about being. In what I do I show who I am. I am not a mixed bag of competences, but I am a living gifted person, and the first among all gifts is the gift of life itself.

We often take for granted the fact that we have life, and forget that it, too, is a gift – the best of all gifts. Like the other gifts we listed at the beginning of this chapter, we need to work at living, to develop the gift of life, so that we become more fully, more richly alive. And as with all gifts, this development can only happen with, through and for others.

Jesus understood this: he understood that this was the very essence of his own life:

I have come that they may have life and have it to the full.
(John 10:10)

THE PROMISE

This process of development was one that the apostles experienced in their time with Jesus. They were, according to the Gospel accounts, ordinary men, invited by Jesus to follow him. Jesus saw in them gifts, gifts which he needed and could use in his own ministry and for the continuation of that ministry once he was gone.

But first, those gifts needed to be cultivated, those qualities that would be useful needed to gain the upper hand on those that were less useful. Think of how Peter was first

highly commended for recognising and declaring that Jesus was the Christ, and then almost immediately had to be reprimanded because he refused to see that death would be the way of the Christ (Mark 8:7-33).

During his public ministry, Jesus kept the apostles near him, giving them ever-deepening insights into his mission. Yet still they found it difficult to comprehend and accept this mission. James and John clearly misunderstood what the future held for them, in asking for the best places in heaven! (Matthew 20:20-23; Mark 10:35-40)

Even as they gathered for the Last Supper, still Jesus had to prompt them: Peter – Peter again – was indignant at the idea of having his feet washed, until Jesus patiently explained that this was what they had been preparing for, to know how to use their gifts to serve.

At that same Last Supper, as presented in John's Gospel, Jesus tried to get the apostles to understand that he had to leave them: 'I shall not be with you much longer … but do not let your hearts be troubled' (John 13:1, John 14:1). It is as if Jesus were making his last will, except what he promises to bequeath to his apostles is the power of the Spirit, the power that has driven and guided him through his ministry, the power to speak the scriptures with authority, to heal …

I shall ask the Father,
and he will give you another Advocate
to be with you for ever,
that Spirit of truth
whom the world can never receive
since it neither sees nor knows him;
but you know him,
because he is with you,
he is in you.
(John 14:16-17)

When the Advocate comes
whom I shall send to you from the
*   Father,*
the Spirit of truth who issues from the
*   Father,*
he will be my witness.
And you too will be my
*   witnesses …*
(John 15:26-27)

However, to make this gift of the Advocate, Jesus had to return to the Father. He had to leave them:

You are sad at heart because I have
*   told you this.*
Still, I must tell you the truth,
it is for your own good that I am going
because unless I go
the Advocate will not come to you;
but if I do go,
I will send him to you.
(John 16:5-7)

To give them his Spirit, Jesus would have to give it up, literally. So, the next day, the same Gospel tells us:

Jesus said,
'It is accomplished';
and bowing his head
he gave up his spirit.
(John 19:30)

The death of Jesus was not the end; the work of training and developing the apostles' gifts reached its final phase, as he appeared to them after his resurrection. However, his work is done, and he must return to the Father. Jesus' final words, in Luke's Gospel, before his ascension were:

Now I am sending down to you
what the Father has promised.
Stay in the city, then,
until you are clothed with power from
*   on high.*
(Luke 24:49)

THE GIFT

Did the apostles really understand what had been promised? They return to Jerusalem, as Jesus instructed. They seem to have understood that Jesus had entrusted them with a mission, to be witnesses to the risen Christ, because Peter takes the initiative of sorting out a replacement for Judas. But there is no evidence of them offering any effective witness. Not, that is, until …

> *When Pentecost day came round*
> *they had all met in one room,*
> *when suddenly*
> *they heard what sounded like*
> *a powerful wind from heaven,*
> *the noise of which filled*
> *the entire house*
> *where they were sitting;*
> *and something appeared to them*
> *that seemed to be*
> *like tongues of fire;*
> *these separated and came to rest*
> *on the head of each of them.*
> *They were filled*
> *with the Holy Spirit,*
> *and began to speak*
> *foreign languages*
> *as the Spirit gave them*
> *the gift of speech.*
>
> *(Acts 2:1-4)*

The Gift, the Spirit, was with them.

The greatest proof of the gift of the Spirit was the change he effected in them. These frightened people, who had been hiding for fear of arrest, now openly started preaching: and what was the essence of the Church's first sermon?

> *Jesus, whom you took and had*
> *crucified ...*
> *You killed him, but God raised him to*
> *life.*
> (Acts 2:24)

The people in the street were flabbergasted, to the extent that they wondered out loud whether the apostles had too much to drink! No, declared Peter, it is not that kind of spirit that has filled us:

> *On the contrary, it is what the prophet*
> *spoke of:*
> *'In the days to come – it is the Lord*
> *who speaks –*
> *I will pour out my spirit on all*
> *humankind.*
> *Their sons and daughters shall*
> *prophesy,*
> *your young men shall see visions,*
> *your old men shall dream dreams.'*
> (Acts 2:16-18, quoting Joel 3:1-5)

The apostles, indeed, were completely transformed. Paul, who would become an apostle later, tried to describe the effect of the gift of the Spirit, which is complete, so transforming:

> *I live now*
> *not with my own life*
> *but with the life of Christ*
> *who lives in me.*
> (Galatians 2:20)

But as with Jesus himself, this gift is not an end in itself. It is not so much power, as empowerment. The moment of Jesus' giving up his spirit on the cross was not the end; filled with that spirit, the apostles could now carry forward the work of Christ, so fulfilling what, in Matthew's Gospel, was Jesus' last command to them:

> *Go, therefore,*
> *make disciples of all nations;*
> *baptise them in the name*
> *of the Father*
> *and of the Son*
> *and of the Holy Spirit,*
> *and teach them to observe all the*
> *commands I gave you.*
> (Matthew 28:19)

HISTORY

The easiest way to explore the history of confirmation is to look at it in three great periods:

- the early Church (first to fourth centuries)
- the growth of the Church (fifth to thirteenth centuries)
- the Middle Ages to which we must of course add:
- confirmation today.

The early Church (first to fourth centuries)

There is no mention of confirmation as a rite separate from baptism in the New Testament. We have to remember that baptismal rites and practices already existed before Christ. What is unique about the baptism which Christ offers is that it links in one *ensemble*, one single process, baptism by water and the descent of the Holy Spirit.

In the Acts of the Apostles (that is, the account of the very earliest days of the

THE EARLY CHURCH

TERTULLIAN
(Late-second-century, North Africa)

Tertullian lived in Carthage in North Africa, at the end of the second century (c. 160-c. 225). He wrote a treatise which is entitled **On Baptism** *but which covers all three of the sacraments of initiation, celebrated in one single ceremony. He bases his theology on the elements of the various rites, which means he offers us a clear glimpse of how what we would now call 'confirmation' was celebrated.*

Immediately we come out of the font, we are anointed with a holy anointing, following the old discipline whereby those entering the priesthood were anointed with oil from a horn, as Aaron was anointed by Moses. This is why they *(the priests)* were called 'Christs', from the word *chrisma* which means anointing; and it is also why the title 'Christ' is given to our Saviour. His was a spiritual anointing, because he was anointed by the Spirit of God the Father . . .

Then there is the imposition of hands over us, invoking the Holy Spirit in a benediction...
(On Baptism: 7,1; 8,1)

THE EARLY CHURCH

HIPPOLYTUS
(Early-third-century, Rome)

Hippolytus, too, offers a description of the threefold rites of initiation, baptism, anointing and first sharing in the Eucharist. Like Tertullian, he speaks of the bishop's laying on of hands on the candidate with a prayer of invocation of the Spirit; and oil is poured on the candidate. Hippolytus also speaks of the candidate being 'sealed' on the forehead, without explaining exactly what this means.

When he *(the candidate)* comes up from the water, he is to be anointed by the presbyter with the oil of thanksgiving, while he *(the presbyter)* says: 'I anoint you with holy oil in the name of Jesus Christ'. Each one then gets dressed, having first dried themselves with a towel, and they come into the church.

The bishop is to lay hands on them, making this invocation: 'Lord God, you have counted these servants worthy to receive the forgiveness of sins by the cleansing of rebirth; now make them worthy to be filled with your Holy Spirit, and send your grace upon them, that they may serve you according to your will; for to you, Father and Son with the Holy Spirit, in the holy Church, is the glory, both now and for ever. Amen.'

Then pouring the consecrated oil from his hand, and laying it on each candidate's head, he is to say: 'I anoint you with holy oil in God the almighty Father and in Jesus Christ and in the Spirit'.

And sealing the candidate on the forehead, he is to give him the kiss of peace as he says: 'The Lord be with you'. And each one who has been sealed is to reply: 'And with your spirit'. The bishop is to do this with each candidate.

From now on, they *(the initiated)* are to pray with all the people; they are not to pray with the faithful until they have received all these things.

When they have prayed, they offer each other the kiss of peace.

(Apostolic Tradition 21-22)

Church), we find that these two elements remain linked together, but in three different ways:

- baptism with water in the name of the Lord is immediately followed by an imposition of hands by an apostle (Acts 8:14-17, 19:5-7)

- baptism by water is seen to have the double effect of forgiving sins and granting the gift of the Spirit (Acts 2:38-41)

- the gift of the Spirit is symbolised by baptism in the name of the Lord (Acts 10:44-48).

There was a spontaneous diversity about the way the rites were celebrated: what mattered was that what was done signified what was really happening: the commitment on the part of the candidate to turn away from a life of sin, and the remission of his or her sins; the commitment to follow Christ; to follow him through life and through death to eternal life with him; all of which is possible only in and with the power of the Spirit.

However, there is one point which is very clear in the Acts of the Apostles: the gift of the Spirit is linked to the gesture of **the imposition of hands** by the apostles.

In the early Church, Christian life was built, lived and worked around the two great sacraments of baptism and the Eucharist. It is within these that what we now call confirmation was found. In one single celebration – most usually during the Easter Vigil – the catechumens were baptised, and then immediately anointed by the bishop (surrounded by his presbyters and deacons); in the Eucharistic celebration that followed, the candidates then received communion for the first time.

By the second century, the imposition of hands was accompanied by an **anointing with chrism**. In the very early days, the direct link with Christ must have been more evident: in many cases, the person imposing hands on the candidates had known Jesus. But as time passed and these eye-witnesses died, the link with Christ was reinforced symbolically.

'Christ' is a title: the English word is derived from the Greek; but the Greek itself was derived from the Hebrew. We also have an English word derived from

that Hebrew word, namely, 'Messiah'. Both 'Christ' and 'Messiah' mean 'anointed'. In a solemn ceremony, where an individual is making a public commitment to follow the way of Jesus, and is recognising Jesus as the Christ, what better way to symbolise this than in being made 'a Christ', in being anointed with chrism.

As time went by, the symbolism of this being marked with chrism was obviously more significant than the laying on of hands, to the extent that gradually the latter was eclipsed and almost disappeared entirely.

Here are some examples of how the rites were celebrated in different ways in different places in this early period:

In the mid-second-century at Carthage (North Africa), initiation was considered as one rite: a baptism by immersion in the power and for the giving of the Spirit, followed by an anointing and the imposition of hands. (See the quote from *On Baptism* by **Tertullian** in the margin column on page 33.)

From the same text which gave us the basis for what is now Eucharistic Prayer 2, we have evidence that in Rome, in the 3rd century, there were two anointings, the first by a presbyter, the second by the bishop, the first before and the second after the laying on of hands. It is at this period that we find the first use of the technical term 'consignation' to define the symbolic gesture of the bishop marking the sign of the cross on the forehead of the newly baptised person. It is also at this time that the kiss of peace between bishop and newly baptised is mentioned. (See the quote from the *Apostolic Tradition* by **Hippolytus** in the margin column left.)

When Ambrose of Milan (340-397) is explaining the rites of initiation to the candidates for initiation in his church, he stresses that it is only through the invocation and in the power of the Spirit that the water becomes an effective sign. Baptism in water (by immersion) is followed by a 'consignation' to signify the 'fulfilment' of the gift of the Spirit. There are two supplementary rites: a washing of the feet and clothing in a white garment. (See the quote from *De Sacramentis* by **Ambrose** in the margin column right.)

Just after Ambrose we have his convert,

Augustine (354-430), for whom, because of personal experience, the whole idea of 'conversion', of completely changing one's life, was particularly significant. In his church at Hippo (North Africa), we find a whole series of rites after baptism, designed to help his community grasp as fully as possible the significance of these sacraments and their power. After baptism, there is an anointing by a priest; a clothing with a white garment (sometimes accompanied by the washing of feet); the laying on of hands, anointing and 'consignation' by the bishop; the kiss of peace; and prayer with all the people.

If you had asked any of these communities to put a name to the sacrament, they would have said simply 'baptism', but for them this covered the complete celebration, not just the rite with water (usually immersion), but the imposition of hands, anointing with oil, plus whatever additional local rites were used to heighten the significance for the people.

The growth of the Church (fourth to thirteenth centuries)

The early Christian communities had grown up in the towns, and the pastoral life of these communities was built around the bishop, assisted by his 'presbyters' and deacons. Until now the bishop had presided over the single continuous rite of baptising, anointing and imposing hands, followed by the Eucharist.

Following Constantine's conversion and his adoption of Christianity as the official religion of his Empire, in the course of the fourth century the Church grew in number and began to spread out of the towns into the countryside. The bishop alone could no longer preside at the liturgical celebrations for the whole of his communities: priests were now ordained and sent with the pastoral ministry of presiding at the Eucharist as the bishop's delegate.

For Christian initiation, the Church had to make a choice between two principles:

either the unity of the celebration, where all of the rites took place successively – in which case both the baptism and the anointing would have to be delegated to the priests;

or to reserve part of the rites to the bishop, and so symbolise his ecclesial role.

In the West, the role of the bishop was seen as the more important value, and so the post-baptismal rites were administered by the bishop. In the course of his visits to the parishes, then, he would administer these rites to all who had been baptised since his previous visit. However, so that it was clear to the people that baptism did imply the gift of the Spirit, the priests did anoint the candidates after baptism.

In the East, the unity of the sacramental celebration was seen as primary. The priest who baptised then continued all the post-baptismal rites, and celebrated the Eucharist, at which the candidate received communion. This is still the practice today among Orthodox Churches, so that even if the candidate is a baby, a tiny drop of consecrated wine is put on his or her lips. The link with the bishop is symbolically maintained, because the oil used for the post-baptismal anointing is consecrated by the bishop.

In the West, then, the priests now presided at the water rite and the Eucharist. But because of the important link in scripture between the gift of the Spirit and the imposition of hands by the apostles, the bishop reserved the anointing and imposition of hands to himself. This was also a reminder that the real local community was not the parish, but the whole diocese, with the bishop as guarantor both of its 'apostolicity' and of unity with the other communities and their bishops.

Probably the oldest evidence for this separation within the rites of initiation comes from Saint Jerome, in the year 382:

'It is the custom of the Churches for the bishop to go out to visit those who, living outside the main towns, have been baptised by presbyters or deacons, so that he might lay hands on them for the invocation of the Holy Spirit . . . without chrism and without the bishop's permission, neither presbyter or deacon have the right to baptise' (*Dialogue with the Luciferians 9*).

When Pope Innocent I writes to his suffragan bishop Decentius at Gubbio in 416, he seems to accept this separation between baptism and the post-baptismal rites as generalised practice. He makes two points,

AMBROSE
(Late-fourth-century, Milan)

Ambrose develops the meaning of 'sealing', insisting that it is a 'spiritual sealing', but without clarifying exactly what rite was involved (though he seems to imply that there was an anointing and that the sign of the cross was made). As in the text by Hippolytus, the Trinity is invoked; but Ambrose goes further, suggesting how the three persons are all at work, differently but together:

God the Father anointed you, the Lord sealed you and put his pledge, the Holy Spirit, into your heart . . .

The spiritual sealing follows *[the washing of the feet]*. You have heard about this in today's reading.* Following the ceremonies of the font, everything has yet to be brought to perfection. This happens when the Holy Spirit is poured out, at the bishop's invocation: 'the spirit of wisdom and understanding, the spirit of right judgement and courage, the spirit of knowledge and reverence, the spirit of holy fear in God's presence.'

*The reading was probably 2 Corinthians 1:21-22, which uses five expressions which would later become the classic vocabulary of the sacrament of confirmation:
'It is God who **confirms** us with you in Christ
and has **anointed** us;
he has **set his seal** upon us
and has **given us the Spirit** in our hearts
as a **pledge/guarantee**.'
(De Sacramentis)

Thomas Aquinas' understanding of confirmation was adopted by the Church, at the Council of Florence (1439), in its Decree for the Armenians (Decretum Pro Armenis):

'In confirmation the Holy Spirit is given for strength, as he was given to the apostles on the day of Pentecost, in order that the Christian may courageously confess the name of Christ. This is why the one to be confirmed is anointed on the forehead (which is the seat of shame) so that the candidate may not be ashamed to confess the name of Christ and above all his cross, which, according to the apostle (Paul) is a stumbling block for the Jews and foolishness for the Gentiles. This is why the candidate is signed with the cross.'

though: the presbyters, when baptising, must use only chrism that the bishop has consecrated; and that only the bishop can sign the forehead with that oil 'for the giving of the Spirit, the Paraclete'.

These pastoral adjustments were to have two consequences:

- The unity of the celebration of Christian initiation was shattered, because the post-baptismal rites were celebrated at different times, and administered by a different minister.

- The order of the rites changed. In the fifth century, adult baptism was still the normal practice, even if it was quite common for children to be baptised. For both adults and children, the 'consignation' was done by the bishop on his next visit to the parish – by which time the baptised would already have shared in the Eucharist for the first time, because, until the twelfth century, baptism was immediately followed by the celebration of the Eucharist.

It is fifth-century France that gave us the word 'confirmation' as a title for a rite that is by now separate. Let us be clear: the verb 'to confirm' already existed and had been used in the context of Christian initiation, for example by Tertullian (c.150-220). However, the word and its synonyms ('to perfect', for example) were used generically, and did not previously have the specific meaning of being the title for a separate rite. Now, at the Council of Riez in 439 (south-east Gaul), we have the use of two separate nouns: 'baptism' and 'confirmation'; similarly the Council of Orange in 441; the Councils at Arles (449-461) use the verb 'to confirm'. We have a Pentecost homily attributed to Faustus, Bishop of Riez (405-490), which clearly shows what was on the mind of the Church; the sense of unease, of needing to justify and explain why and how baptism and confirmation are separate rites. The homily poses the question explicitly: 'After the mystery of baptism, what use can the ministry of confirmation be?' The homily offers an answer, and speaks of a gift of the Spirit with the imposition of hands by the bishop which is different from that of baptism: 'In the baptismal font, the Holy Spirit has given us the fullness of innocence; in confirmation he

offers an increase in grace. In baptism we are reborn to life; after baptism we are confirmed for combat. In baptism we are washed; after baptism we are strengthened.'

This 'personal' rather than 'ecclesial' interpretation (that is, confirming the individual person to enable them better to fight and struggle against the forces of evil) was not the only way the now separate rite was interpreted. Bishop Rabanus Maurus of Mayence (780-856) – who is thought to be the author of the great hymn to the Holy Spirit, *Veni Creator Spiritus* (Come, Holy Ghost, Creator come) – invited his people to see it as a sharing in the apostolic experience of Pentecost, a sacrament of 'overwhelming fullness'.

What might have remained an interesting local interpretation, which made sense for Faustus and his people in fifth-century Gaul, by a quirk of history would assume immense importance in the history of the theology of confirmation. This homily text was included in an anthology compiled in the ninth century, and was (falsely) attributed to Pope Melchiades. For ninth-century contemporaries this gave magisterial authority to this interpretation. When the Scholastics subsequently came to explore confirmation, they thought that this represented the Church's only traditional teaching.

By the twelfth century the more individualistic interpretation became the standard. This went hand in hand with an increasing separation between baptism and confirmation. Infant baptism was now the norm; dioceses were bigger, so it was now two or three years before confirmation by the bishop. It was during this era that communion was no longer offered to children, but held back until they reach 'the age of reason'.

Middle Ages

The early Middle Ages is the time of the Scholastics, working to understand, to build a theology of the Church and all she does, especially the sacraments. There was a clear ceremony of anointing with chrism by the bishop, accompanied by a formula of words; wherever they found the expression 'confirmation' in the tradition of the Church, they saw this rite, not realising they were doing so anachronistically. The

Scholastic method was one, par excellence, of defining by categorising. Confirmation is defined as one of the seven sacraments distinct from baptism. However, the theologians of this era differed in their explanations of the purpose and the effect of the sacrament. Did the sacraments give the gifts of the Spirit, or did it give the Spirit himself? What was the sense of the sacrament's name? That is, who or what was being confirmed? In other words, this was a time when the Church was reflecting on the sense and significance of what had become standard practice.

The upheaval of the Reformation did not leave the sacrament of confirmation unaffected. In 1520 Martin Luther argues that it cannot be considered a sacrament, because it lacks two essential features: it was not explicitly instituted by Christ; and there is no promise by Christ of a grace linked to the visible sign (see quote from *The Babylonian Captivity of the Church* to the right). Luther does not reject the use of a confirmation ceremony, but simply denies it can be called a sacrament. In addition, he links a symbolic laying on of hands to the period of post-baptismal catechesis (which he restored), making it the ceremonial conclusion to this period of initiation, and a sign that the baptised was now fully initiated and ready to receive the Eucharist for the first time (see margin column right).

He may have denied the sacramental nature of confirmation, but perhaps the adjusted process he proposed had a greater coherence than existing Catholic practice. We need to remember that the ordinary people knew confirmation, not necessarily in its full and proper form as set out in the rituals, but as actually practised by often lax clergy. There is one account, for example, of the bishop arriving in the village, and not even bothering to get down from his horse to make a perfunctory laying on of hands. Compared to such abuses, one can imagine the natural appeal of Luther's proposals! In all events, there was a falloff in the practice of confirmation at this period.

The Council of Trent (1545-1563) faced up to the double question posed by Luther: the doctrinal one and that of actual pastoral practice. The Council declares solemnly that confirmation is one of the seven sacraments. It also declares that the normal minister of this sacrament should be the bishop. However, the Council is silent on the institution of confirmation, and says nothing about the relationship between confirmation and baptism, nor about the difference between these sacraments. In fact, the most pressing problem facing the Council was to restore the practice of confirmation, which had been in decline, largely because of the Reformation. The ritual for confirmation, as approved by Trent is basically the fifth-century Roman rite of 'consignation'.

In its Catechism (1566), Trent declares that any baptised person can receive confirmation, although it recommends it be deferred until age 7: this is because confirmation is presented as 'preparing and arming us when called upon to fight for the faith of Christ, for which no one would consider children still without the age of reason to be qualified'. However, it should not be postponed beyond the age of 12.

Standard practice, then, was to receive confirmation at about the age of 7 or 8, which was also the age at which first communion was celebrated. In the course of the seventeenth-century, we find first communion being delayed to the age of 12 or 13. This meant that confirmation was being received before first communion. It is in 1910, when Pope Pius X moves first communion forward to the age of reason (normally age 7), that the order is changed, and becomes normative: baptism-first communion-confirmation.

Confirmation today

As we explore the Rite of Confirmation, as revised at the demand of Vatican II, we can hear constant echoes from the past, the work of our predecessors in the faith across centuries, bearing fruit in the shape of today's celebration.

Firstly, confirmation is now firmly re-established as being part of the process of Christian initiation:

> *Those who have been baptised*
> *continue on the path of Christian*
> *   initiation*
> *through the sacrament of confirmation.*
> (Rite of Confirmation, 1)

**MARTIN LUTHER
(1483-1546)**

'In looking for sacraments instituted by God, we find no reason to include confirmation among the sacraments. For there to be a sacrament there must first and foremost be a divine promise, which in turn imposes on us an obligation in faith. But nowhere do we read that Christ ever formulated any kind of promise concerning confirmation, although he himself certainly laid hands on many people . . .

(The Babylonian Captivity of the Church)

AFTER THE REFORMATION

Though refusing to accept confirmation as a sacrament and in rejecting what was then current practice as 'an abuse and an empty ceremony', the Reformers did see a great value in a rite which 'confirmed' the faith of those baptised, and in particular which signified that they were now ready to share in the Eucharist.

*For example, in the **Brandenburg Church Order** (1540), confirmation is encouraged as a rite for: 'those who have been baptised and reached an age when they know what they ought to believe, how to pray, and also know that they ought to be leading a Christian life, behaving in an honest manner, as set out in the catechism . . .'*

This examining of the baptised was to be done by the bishop, who would 'confirm' those who matched these criteria, and who would admonish the parents of those who were inadequately prepared.

CRANMER'S PRAYER BOOK (1549)

'None shall hereafter be confirmed but such as can say in their mother tongue the articles of the faith, the Lord's Prayer and the Ten Commandments, and can also answer to such questions of the short catechism as the bishop shall by his discretion oppose them in.'

In fact, this rubric was added due to the influence of Martin Bucer, from whom Cranmer had asked advice. For Bucer, what mattered was that this public statement should be the expression of what the person really believed: 'Not a few children make a confession of faith of this kind with no more understanding of the faith than some parrot uttering his 'Hello' . . . It is surely to be wished that children should not be admitted to that public and solemn confession of faith and obedience to Christ (i.e. to confirmation) before they have also demonstrated their faith by their lives and conduct . . .'

Secondly, the parallel with Pentecost, and the insistence that it is the Holy Spirit which is received through this sacrament:

In this sacrament
they receive the Holy Spirit,
whom the Lord sent upon the apostles
at Pentecost.
(Rite of Confirmation, 1)

Thirdly, the fruits of the sacrament are explicitly related to Christ (i.e. 'christologically') and to the Church (i.e. 'ecclesially'):

This giving of the Holy Spirit
conforms believers more perfectly to
Christ
for the building up of his body in faith
and love.
(Rite of Confirmation, 2)

The ecclesial dimension of confirmation is also underlined by the importance given to the bishop being the 'original' and 'ordinary' minister of confirmation:

The original minister of confirmation
is the bishop.
Ordinarily the sacrament is
administered by the bishop
so that there will be a more evident
relationship
to the first pouring forth of the Holy
Spirit on Pentecost.
After the apostles were filled with the
Holy Spirit,
they themselves gave the Spirit to the
faithful
through the laying on of their hands.
Thus the reception of the Spirit
through the ministry of the bishop
shows the close bond
which unites the confirmed to the
Church
and the mandate
to be witnesses of Christ
among men and women.
(Rite of Confirmation, 7)

THE RITE OF CONFIRMATION
OUTLINE

It is, happily, standard practice for the Rite of Confirmation to be celebrated within Mass, in which case it comes after the Liturgy of the Word and before the Liturgy of the Eucharist. The Rite says:

Ordinarily confirmation takes place
within Mass
in order to express more clearly
the fundamental connection of this
sacrament
with the entirety of Christian
initiation.
The latter reaches its culmination
in the communion of the body and
blood of Christ.
The newly confirmed should therefore
participate in the Eucharist
which completes their Christian
initiation.
(Rite of Confirmation, 13)

Here, then, is an outline of the complete celebration:

LITURGY OF THE WORD
SACRAMENT OF CONFIRMATION
  Presentation of the candidates
  Homily
  Renewal of baptismal promises
  Laying on of hands
  Anointing with chrism
  General intercessions
LITURGY OF THE EUCHARIST

The sponsor

Before exploring the celebration, there is one prerequisite of confirmation that deserves our attention. Normally, every candidate for confirmation should have a sponsor, who has a symbolic role during the celebration. It is the sponsor who brings the candidate to receive the sacrament, and who presents him or her to the bishop for anointing. This role within the sacrament is symbolic of the duties of the sponsor to help the candidate fulfil his or her baptismal promises faithfully under the influence of the Holy Spirit.

Given the role the sponsor has to play, they should be chosen accordingly:

– if at all possible, the sponsor should be the same person who was godparent at baptism. This would express more clearly the essential relationship between baptism and confirmation.

– the sponsor should be someone who understands the commitment the candidate is making, and should therefore have already passed through this same commitment themselves. In others words, the sponsor should be a fully initiated member of the Church, baptised, confirmed and having made their first communion.

– for the same reason, the sponsor needs to be mature enough to assume this responsibility. Canon Law suggests this means the sponsor be at least 16.

Liturgy of the Word

The Liturgy of the Word is not just a routine element, but should have a heightened importance in the celebration of confirmation. Firstly, because it is 'from the hearing of the Word of God that the many-faceted power of the Spirit flows upon the Church and upon each one of the baptised and confirmed' (Rite of Confirmation, 13). Secondly, in this sacrament the candidates are publicly accepting the mandate to be witnesses of Christ and to conform themselves more exactly on Christ: it is in the Word, especially the Gospels, that they will discover God's will, his mandate for them, and will learn more about Christ to whom they are to give witness (see Rite of Confirmation, 13).

The Lectionary provides a selection of suitable texts for the Liturgy of the Word (see column to the right). The readings may also be taken, in part or in whole, from the Mass of the day (especially if confirmation is celebrated on a Sunday).

Presentation of the candidates

The candidates for confirmation are presented to the bishop. It is far better if the candidates can be called and presented to the bishop individually – with their sponsors, in the case of children or young adults. This would help to give personal sense to the candidate of that value which, as our exploration has revealed, the Church in the West thought so important: that the minister be the bishop because he is the head of the local Church. Where there are too many candidates for an individual presentation, they could still be called by name. Only if there are very many candidates should they be presented *en bloc*.

Homily

As always, the essential function of the homily is to explain the readings: within this celebration, it should also lead not only the candidates but the whole assembly to a deeper understanding of the meaning of confirmation.

For the candidates, the homily should also be a reminder of the implications of being confirmed:

– to be witnesses before all the world of Christ's suffering, death and resurrection

– to live a life that reflects the goodness of Christ

– to use the gifts that the Spirit gives them for the building up of Christ's body, the Church, in unity and love (see Rite of Confirmation, 22).

Renewal of baptismal promises

The renewal of the baptismal promises is a very concrete expression of the essential link between baptism and confirmation. If those being confirmed were baptised as children, these vows will have been on their behalf by their sponsors. It is a public proclamation of fully accepting their baptism and all that it signifies: accepting the love of God shown in baptism; accepting the implications of following Christ, and showing the same openness as he himself did to the Spirit in their lives.

The renewal of promises follows the classic, if shortened form. There is first a

---

SCRIPTURE READINGS FOR CONFIRMATION FIRST READING

OLD TESTAMENT

[used outside Easter season]

Isaiah 11:1-4
The gifts of the Spirit.

Isaiah 42:1-3
Here is my servant,
I have endowed with my spirit.

Isaiah 61:1-3, 6, 8-9
The Lord has anointed me
and sent me.

Ezekiel 36:24-28
I shall put my spirit in you.
You shall be my people
and I shall be your God.

Joel 2:23, 26-3:3
I will pour out my spirit on all.

NEW TESTAMENT

[in Easter season]

Acts 1:3-8
You will receive power
when the Spirit comes
and be my witnesses.

Acts 2:1-6, 14, 22-3, 32-3
They were all filled with the Holy Spirit.

Acts 8:1, 4, 14-17
The apostles laid hands on them,
and they received the Holy Spirit.

Acts 10:1, 33-4, 37-44
The Holy Spirit came down
on all the listeners.

Acts 19:1-6
Paul laid hands on them
and the Holy Spirit came
down on them.

renunciation of evil. Then the candidates are invited to affirm positively their faith. This is usually an adaptation of the ancient formula of the Apostles' Creed, expressed in a question and answer dialogue:

Do you believe in God the Father
almighty,
Creator of heaven and earth?
I do.
Do you believe in Jesus Christ,
his only Son, our Lord,
who was born of the Virgin Mary,
was crucified, died and was buried,
rose from the dead,
and is now seated at the right hand of
the Father?
I do.
Do you believe in the Holy Spirit,
the Lord, the giver of life,
who came upon the apostles at
Pentecost
and today is given to you
sacramentally in confirmation?
I do.
Do you believe in the holy Catholic
Church,
the communion of saints,
the forgiveness of sins,
the resurrection of the body,
and life everlasting?
I do.

The bishop then shows his acceptance of the candidates' profession of faith, and invites the whole assembly to join him in doing the same. For example, all may sing together:

This is our faith.
This is the faith of the Church.
We are proud to profess it
in Jesus Christ our Lord.

Alternatively, the bishop may say this, to which the congregation reply:

Amen.

Laying on of hands

After the candidates have professed their baptismal faith, any concelebrating priests stand near the bishop, who invites the assembly to pray:

My dear friends,
in baptism God our Father gave the
new birth

of eternal life to his chosen sons and
daughters.
Let us pray to our Father
that he will pour out the Holy Spirit
to strengthen his sons and daughters
with his gifts
and anoint them
to be more like Christ the Son of God.

All pray in silence, and then the bishop, together with those priests who will assist him in ministering this sacrament, lay hands on all the candidates, by extending their hands over them. This is a very ancient symbolic gesture, going back into Old Testament times. Its original meaning of empowerment came to acquire a special significance in the New Testament: it is empowerment by the Spirit. The gesture should be familiar to the candidates, from the twofold 'epiclesis', the invocation of the Spirit, during the eucharistic prayer (see the chapter on the Eucharist, particularly page 56).

The bishop alone then prays aloud:

All-powerful God,
Father of our Lord Jesus Christ,
by water and the Holy Spirit
you freed your sons and daughters from
sin
and gave them new life.
Send your Holy Spirit upon them
to be their helper and guide.
Give them the spirit of wisdom and
understanding,
the spirit of right judgement and
courage,
the spirit of knowledge and reverence.
Fill them with the spirit of wonder
and awe in your presence.
We ask you this through Christ our
Lord.
Amen.

The gifts of the Spirit are those promised by the prophet Isaiah (see Isaiah 11:2-3, which is one of the suggested readings for the Liturgy of the Word); this promise is first fulfilled in Christ; thereafter, it is fulfilled for all the Church on Pentecost; and today, here and now, for these candidates:

Wisdom:
the gift to judge things in the way God
does

Understanding:
the gift to interpret correctly what God
teaches through his Word

Right judgement:
> the gift to know what to do, especially when faced with difficult situations

Courage:
> the gift of strength to do what is right, no matter how hard this may be

Knowledge:
> the gift to see the world as it really is

Reverence:
> the gift to love God and each other as we should

Awe and wonder:
> the gift to recognise and appreciate the presence of God, and his greatness.

The coming of the Spirit on the Apostles at Pentecost was very dramatic – for example, they began to speak in other languages and in prophetic words. The coming of the Spirit in confirmation may be less dramatic, and is not usually marked by the gift of the tongues! However:

> *his coming is known in faith . . .
> Christ gives varied gifts to his
> Church and the Spirit distributes
> them among the members of Christ's
> body, so as to build up the holy
> people of God in unity and love.*

(Rite of Confirmation, 22)

Anointing with chrism

Chrism is a mixture of olive oil and balm. The first instructions concerning holy oil for anointing given to Moses by God in Exodus list both ingredients and how to prepare them (Exodus 30:22-30). Still today, chrism is basically a mixture of oil and perfume. This perfumed ointment, together with the other holy oils (oil of catechumens and oil of the sick) is blessed by the bishop during the Mass of Chrism, which traditionally takes place on Holy Thursday morning. (In some dioceses it is celebrated earlier in Holy Week, so that the oils can be distributed to all the parishes in time for their use at the Easter Vigil.)

For the anointing, normally each candidate goes to the bishop, though the bishop may go to the individual candidates. The sponsor places his or her right hand on the candidate's shoulder.

Either the candidate or the sponsor gives the candidate's name to the bishop: in some places, the candidates wear name-badges, often in a suitably symbolic form (for example, in the shape of a dove).

The bishop dips his right thumb in the chrism and makes the sign of the cross on the candidate's forehead, saying:

> ...... [Candidate's name],
> *be sealed with the Gift of the
> Holy Spirit.*

This is a very ancient form of words, dating back at least to the fourth or fifth century. It is quoted, for example by Cyril, Bishop of Jerusalem (middle- to late-fourth-century), in his sermons preparing

THE SIGNIFICANCE OF CHRISM

The consecration of the sacred chrism is an important action that precedes the celebration of Confirmation, but is in a certain way a part of it. It is the bishop who, in the course of the chrism Mass of Holy Thursday, consecrates the sacred chrism for his whole diocese. In some Eastern Churches this consecration is even reserved to the patriarch: The Syriac liturgy of Antioch expresses the epiclesis for the consecration of the sacred chrism *(myron)* in this way:

'Father . . . send your Holy Spirit on us and on this oil which is before us and consecrate it, so that it may be for all who are anointed and marked with it holy myron, priestly myron, royal myron, anointing with gladness, clothing with light, a cloak of salvation, a spiritual gift, the sanctification of souls and bodies, imperishable happiness, the indelible seal, a buckler of faith, and a fearsome helmet against all the works of the adversary.'

Catholic Catechism, 1297

candidates for initiation. It is the same form of words that is still used today in the Churches of the Byzantine rite. This form of words is used because, in the words of Pope Paul VI:

> *the gift of the Spirit himself is expressed and the outpouring of the Spirit which took place on the day of Pentecost is recalled.*
> (Apostolic Constitution *Divine consortium naturae*)

Three things are happening at once, and their apparent simplicity belies the depth of their meaning. There is plenty here for the candidate to explore in his quest to understand the sacrament!

– an **anointing** with perfumed oil, which shows that

> *by Confirmation, Christians, that is, those who are anointed, share more completely in the mission of Jesus Christ and the fullness of the Holy Spirit with which he is filled, so that their lives may give off 'the aroma of Christ'* [2 Corinthians 2:16] **(Catechism 1294)**

the words interpret this as 'sealing': seals are used to authenticate documents, such as Acts of Parliament, wills, treaties between nations. The seal is the symbol of a person, but especially of that person's authority and power. Another way to translate 'sealing' in English would be 'branding': in other words, marking the ownership of something of someone. Beyond these 'ordinary' but no less symbolic meanings of 'seal', there is the example of Christ himself, who declared that he was marked with his Father's seal (John 6:27). Christians are also marked with a seal:

> *'It is God who establishes us with you in Christ and has commissioned us; he has put his seal on us and given us his Spirit in our hearts as a guarantee' (2 Cor 1:22 cf. Eph 1:13; 4:30). This seal of the Holy Spirit marks our total belonging to Christ, our enrolment in his service for ever, as well as the promise of divine protection in the great eschatological trial* [Apocalypse 7:2-3, 9:4; Ezekiel 9:4-6].
> **(Catechism 1296)**

The sign that is marked on the forehead of the candidate is **the sign of the cross.** Confirmation gives us:

> *a special strength of the Holy Spirit to spread and defend the faith by word and action as true witnesses of Christ, to confess the name of Christ boldly, and never to be ashamed of the Cross* [Lumen Gentium 11, 12].
> **(Catechism 1303)**

This part of the rite is completed by an age-old gesture, the exchange of a **sign of peace.** This gesture is familiar to us today, since it was restored after Vatican II as a practice to be shared among all participants at the Sunday Eucharist. It had long since died out as a sign that was exchanged between the laity and the clergy. However, it did survive in a somewhat strange form in the pre-Vatican II rite of confirmation. The traditional exchange had been reduced to the bishop touching the candidate on the cheek. But with the effort to give sense to confirmation as a sacrament on its own and the interpretation that it 'strengthened' the Christian to be a 'soldier' of Christ, this gesture, a tap on the cheek, was seen as meaning the confirmed should be prepared to suffer for the sake of Christ and his gospel!

What is worthwhile in this interpretation is already amply signified by the sign of the cross marked on the forehead. It is surely more important, more valuable to see this exchange between bishop and the confirmed as symbolising his acceptance, as head of the local Church, of this decisive step by which they are bonded more closely to the Church.

General intercessions or Prayer of the Faithful

When the anointing of all the candidates is completed, all stand, and the bishop invites the assembly to pray for the needs of the world, for the Church in its task to serve the world, and especially for those who have been newly confirmed.

The Rite of Confirmation offers a range of appropriate intentions for prayer, which may be replaced by intentions written by the community for the occasion.

In all events, it would be appropriate if the intentions were pronounced by someone who has been closely involved in the preparation of those now confirmed, or by some of the newly confirmed.

Here is the concluding prayer by the bishop which the Rite of Confirmation suggests:

God our Father,
you sent your Holy Spirit upon the
*   apostles,*
and through them and their successors
you give your Spirit to your people.
May his work begun at Pentecost
continue to grow in the hearts of all
*   who believe.*

Liturgy of the Eucharist

The Liturgy of the Eucharist continues in the usual way, except that there are moments which should be particularly significant for the newly-confirmed, or when it is appropriate that they take a particularly active part.

- some of the newly confirmed should be among those who bring the gifts to the altar

- if Eucharistic Prayer I is used, the Roman Missal gives a special form of 'Father accept this offering …'

- *the saying of the Lord's Prayer by the newly confirmed with the rest of the people is also of very great importance, because it is the Spirit who prays in us, and in the Spirit the Christian says 'Abba, Father'.*
(Rite of Confirmation, 13)

- to mark in a special way the link between confirmation and the Eucharist, it would be good if the newly confirmed, together with their sponsors, parents, family and catechists, receive communion under both kinds.

EUCHARIST
The signs of bread and wine

BREAD AND WINE

The oldest account of the Eucharist, of the Last Supper that Jesus shared with his disciples before he died, is from Paul's First Letter to the Corinthians:

On the same night that he was betrayed,
the Lord Jesus took some bread . . .
In the same way he took the cup . . .
(1 Corinthians 11:24-25).

Jesus was celebrating Passover with his disciples, and the bread and the cup were already rich in symbolism, were already full of promise.

Passover was the annual commemoration of the great escape from Egypt. Central to the Passover is the lamb, whose blood, sprinkled on the door-posts, will save the first-born (because the angel of death will 'pass over'). But alongside the lamb, there is the unleavened bread. Unleavened because there is no time to wait for the yeast to rise, God's people must be up and away. Unleavened bread is the sign that this is a pilgrim people, on its way to a freedom that has not yet been completely achieved. It is bread that implies a promise (cf. Exodus 13).

The Promised Land did not await the Israelites at the other side of the Red Sea: they had to make the desert crossing. When the people, found themselves on the brink of starvation, God gave them manna, a word whose origin is playfully described in the Book of Exodus as being derived from what the Israelites said when they first saw it: '*Man hu* – What is it?' Its name is less important than how it is described: Moses tells the people 'That is *the bread the Lord gives you* to eat.' The manna was a daily bread. The episode concludes with the note 'The sons of Israel ate manna for forty years, up to the time they reached the frontier of the land of Canaan'. This is not yet the bread of the Promised Land, it is bread that implies a promise (cf. Exodus 16).

Immediately after receiving the Ten Commandments, when Moses is explaining to the Israelites that they are a people set apart, he promises them that in return for keeping God's Law faithfully, God will be true to the covenant and the kindness he promised their fathers. Listed among the signs of God's love is that he will 'bless the fruit of your soil, your corn, your wine.' (cf. Deuteronomy 7, especially verse 13). The juxtaposition is not a coincidence: *corn* (bread) and *wine*, necessary for life, are seen as God-given. But beyond that, among creation, God has chosen a people, has made a covenant with them, which is symbolised by abundance of bread and wine. Bread and wine are concrete signs of the covenant promise.

When the people did cross the Jordan and reached the Promised Land, on the morrow of Passover, they celebrated and 'they tasted the produce of that country, unleavened bread . . .'; from that time, the manna stopped falling (Joshua 5:11-12).

Wine, too, was symbolic. It is only after the purification of the Flood, and creation is starting anew, that we have wine: 'Noah, a tiller of the soil, was the first to plant the vine . . .' (cf. Genesis 9, especially verse 20). The sequel of this story is rather inglorious, but already we have the suggestion that the vine is the sign of new life. Jesus will later exploit this earthy metaphor in several parables.

In his preaching and teaching, Jesus was able to call on bread and wine, both because they were part of the staple diet of his listeners, but also because they already had symbolic meaning.

The Gospel accounts of the multiplication of the loaves, a superabundance of bread, are a clear prefiguring of the Eucharist as well as being carefully crafted to be an echo of Exodus 16. Indeed in John 6, a direct comparison will be made

The vine that is planted in the earth bears fruit in its season, and the grain of wheat that falls into the soil and cracks open there rises up multiplied by the Spirit of God who holds all things together.

The bread and wine are wisely put to man's use, and when they receive the Word of God they become the Eucharist, that is, the body and blood of Christ.

So too our bodies that are nourished by the Eucharist are placed in the earth and dissolve into it, but they shall rise when their time comes, for the Word of God will make them rise for the glory of the Father, who clothes this mortal body in immortality and gives this corruptible body an unmerited incorruptibility, since the power of God is made perfect in weakness.

Irenaeus (c.130-c.200), bishop of Lyons from c.178
Adversus Hæreses, V, 2, 3

between the manna received in the desert and the bread given by Jesus, both by those who receive the bread and by Jesus himself in this discussion with them.

The crowd said, 'What sign will you give to show us that we should believe in you? What work will you do? Our fathers had manna in the desert; as scripture says "He gave them bread from heaven to eat".'
Jesus answered:
'I tell you solemnly,
it was not Moses who gave you bread from heaven,
it is my Father who gives you the bread from heaven,
the true bread;
for the bread of God is that which comes down from heaven
and gives life to the world.'
'Sir,' they said, 'give us that bread always.'
Jesus answered:
'I am the bread of life.
He who comes to me will never be hungry;
he who believes in me will never thirst . . .
I am the bread of life.
Your fathers ate the manna in the desert
and they are dead;
but this is the bread that comes down from heaven,
so that a man may eat it and not die.
I am the living bread which has come down from heaven.
Anyone who eats this bread will live for ever . . .
This is the bread which came from heaven;
not like the bread your ancestors ate: they are dead,
but anyone who eats this bread will live for ever.'
(John 6:30-32, 35, 48-51, 58)

Already John's Gospel has opened Christ's public ministry with water turned into the abundance of wine at the wedding in Cana (cf. John 2). And by the parallels

of language, John links this water and wine with the blood and water that will flow from the side of Christ (John 19:34).

Alongside this teaching in action, there are Jesus' words. There is the parable of the vineyard, left to the wicked husbandmen, who end up killing the son (Matthew 21:33-43; Mark 12:1-11; Luke 20:9-18). In contrast to the superabundance that Jesus offers, here the vineyard fails to produce fruit for the master. In John's Gospel, the same theme is treated in the discourse on the true vine (cf. John 15), which follows the Last Supper.

THE LAST SUPPER

Jesus, with his apostles gathered around him, fulfils what the Jewish Law demands:

When the hour came, Jesus took his place at table, and the apostles with him. And he said to them, 'I have longed to eat this passover with you before I suffer; because I tell you, I shall not eat it again until it is fulfilled in the kingdom of God.' Then taking a cup, he gave thanks and said, 'Take this and share it among you, because from now on, I tell you, I shall not drink wine until the kingdom of God comes.'
(Luke 22:14-18)

Jesus celebrates the Passover, the great feast commemorating God's faithfulness to his covenant, the feast with its symbolic bread and its cups of blessing. To the promise that the passover already enshrines, Jesus adds another:

Then he took some bread, and when he had given thanks, he broke it and gave it to them, saying, 'This is my body which will be given for you; do this as a memorial of me.' He did the same with the cup after supper, and said, 'This cup is the new covenant in my blood which will be poured out for you.'
(Luke 22:19-20)

The promise that Jesus makes in words during the Last Supper he fulfils in deed the next day on the cross: his body is given; his blood poured.

The original passover was a ritual celebration, a memorial of God's saving power by which the first-born are saved by the blood of the lamb, and the people of God delivered from slavery; so too the new passover of Christ is to be celebrated as a memorial of the salvation achieved by the blood of the Lamb, the first-born from the dead, who leads the new People of God out of the slavery of sin.

> *By celebrating the Last Supper*
> *with his apostles*
> *in the course of the Passover meal,*
> *Jesus gave the Jewish Passover*
> *its definitive meaning.*
> *Jesus' passing over to his father*
> *by his death and resurrection,*
> *the new Passover,*
> *is anticipated in the Supper*
> *and celebrated in the Eucharist,*
> *which fulfils the Jewish Passover*
> *and anticipates the final Passover*
> *of the Church*
> *in the glory of the kingdom.*
>
> (Catechism 1340)

'DO THIS IN MEMORY OF ME'

Let us return to the oldest account of the Eucharist, given by Paul. He is careful to begin:

This is what I received from the Lord, and in turn passed on to you: that on the same night that he was betrayed, the Lord Jesus took some bread, and thanked God for it and broke it, and he said, 'This is my body, which is for you; do this as a memorial of me.'

In the same way he took the cup after the supper, and said, 'This cup is the covenant in my blood. Whenever you drink it, do this as a memorial of me.'

Until the Lord comes, therefore, every time you eat this bread and drink this cup, you are proclaiming his death.

(1 Corinthians 11:23-26)

Paul speaks of a tradition, something he has received from the Lord and which he in turn passed on. This tradition, as given by Paul contains the command, not just once but twice: '*Do this as a memorial of me.*' It is concluded by a solemn reminder that whenever it is done, it is a proclamation of the Lord's death until he comes again.

The apostolic perception of what Christ has commanded could not be clearer! This memorial is frequent, '*every time*'; and it will last until the end of time, '*until the Lord comes*'. The memorial is a proclamation of Christ's passover: '*you are proclaiming his death*'. Celebrating this memorial is understood to have been a command, a 'tradition', which the apostles had from Christ himself.

With a simplicity which must have meant that this tradition was fully understood and accepted, Luke in Acts says that the very first Christian community (the apostles plus those baptised on Pentecost) remained

faithful to the teaching of the apostles, to the brotherhood, to the breaking of bread and to the prayers . . . They went as a body to the Temple every day but met in their houses for the breaking of bread.

(Acts 2:42, 46)

The frequency of this celebration is indicated later in Acts:

On the first day of the week, we met to break bread . . .

(Acts 20:7)

THE EUCHARIST
(Rome c.150)

On the day we call the day of the sun, all who live in the city or the countryside assemble, and the memoirs of the apostles or the writings of the prophets are read for as long as time permits.

When the reader has finished, he who presides over those who have gathered together addresses us, admonishing us to imitate these splendid things.

Then we all stand together and pray and, as we have said earlier, when we have finished praying, bread, wine and water are brought up. He who presides offers prayers of thanksgiving (makes Eucharist), according to his ability, and the people give their assent with an 'Amen!' Next the gifts which have been eucharistised are distributed, and each one shares in them, and they are also taken, by the deacons, to those who are absent.

(Justin, *First Apology 67, 3-5*)

When Justin, a lay philosopher who would later be martyred, was writing to explain or justify the Eucharist to Jews in the middle of the second century, he states clearly that the Eucharist had its origin in the command of Jesus:

> *the Eucharist which our Lord Jesus Christ commanded us to offer in memory of the passion he underwent for the sake of those who are cleansed from evil.*
> (Justin, *Dialogue with Trypho 41, 1*)

Justin also wrote explaining the Eucharist to pagans:

> *. . . that in the memoirs which the apostles composed and which we call 'gospels' they were commissioned in this way; that Jesus took bread and having given thanks, said 'Do this in memory of me; this is my body'; in the same way he took the cup and, having given thanks, said 'This is my blood'. These he gave to them (i.e. to the apostles) alone.*
> (Justin, *First Apology 66, 3*)

Notice how Justin emphasises that this is not something the Church has invented, it is something 'commissioned' by Jesus.

In the next chapter of his *First Apology*, Justin describes with elegant simplicity the essential features of the Eucharist of the time (i.e. mid-second-century): gathering on Sunday; Liturgy of the Word with homily and Prayer of the Faithful; liturgy of the Eucharist with presentation of gifts, the eucharistic prayer and the distribution of communion (see the full quote in the left-hand column).

Roughly a century later, in the **Apostolic Tradition**, Hippolytus recounts the celebration of the Eucharist at Rome. For the first time, in this text, we have a developed liturgical prayer, which forms the basis for our modern day Eucharistic Prayer II.

The third century was the era of great diversity in liturgy: Justin had already said that the one who presided offered thanks 'according to his ability'. No doubt the churches sought in those who were to pray in the name of the Church the charism of being able to do it well. In the East, there were exceptional pastors like Basil, John Chrysostom, Cyril of Jerusalem and Cyril of Alexandria.

Looking back across the history of how the Eucharist has been celebrated since the apostles to the modern day, we can simplify the maze of liturgical differences by identifying four great liturgical families.

In the East, there were the two great families centred around Antioch (Syria) and Alexandria (Egypt). In the West, there was a family centred around Italy/North Africa, and another centred around western Europe. Within each of these families, local rites could be identified. For the West, in the Italian/African family there were the Roman rite, the Ambrosian rite (Milan) and the Augustinian rite (Hippo, North Africa). The other rites that existed in the West were the Mozarabic (Spain) the Gallican (Gaul) and the Celtic (Ireland, Scotland, Wales and Britanny).

In the West, the diversity died out in favour of the Roman rite during the fifth and sixth centuries. Three great collections of liturgical texts date from this period: the *Verona Sacramentary*, attributed to Pope Leo I (440-461); the *Gelasian Sacramentary*, so named because it was attributed to Pope Gelasius (482-496); and the *Gregorian Sacramentary*, compiled around 592 by Pope Gregory the Great (590-604). The latter book was to be influential in establishing the Roman rite in preference to other rites, because when Charlemagne was converted, he decided to use liturgical uniformity as a lever for the political unity of his empire. On the presumption that the papal liturgy was the best, he requested a copy: Pope Hadrian I (772-795) sent him a revised copy of the Gregorian Sacramentary.

This master copy was entrusted to scribes, to make copies for the Empire. However, in the transcription, various elements of the Gallican tradition were slipped in.

These collections contained only the liturgical texts, without what we nowadays call rubrics or instructions on how to celebrate. In the ninth century copies began to appear with directions for the rites added. At the time, these were known as '*ordines*'.

In the tenth century, complete collections, using the material that was previously found in the separate ritual collections, were compiled, principally on the basis of the *Ordines*. By now, Rome had fallen into the dark ages; in the second half of the tenth century the so-called Romano-German Pontifical reached Rome, where, because the previous genuine liturgical sources had been lost, it was extremely welcome. The Roman rite thus came home to Rome, but not, as was supposed, the old Roman liturgy; rather the liturgy that had made a great detour through the Gallo-Frank lands, picking up many elements from those traditions. It became the rite of Rome.

When Gregory VII (1073-1085) took the Church in hand, he asked all bishops to use the liturgical practice of Rome. It was a slow process, and it was not until the thirteenth century that its adoption was widespread.

In fact, uniformity was not imposed by the Church until the *Roman Missal* of Pius V (1580), and the various other ritual books (the *Pontifical* in 1596; the *Roman Ritual* in 1614), following the Council of Trent. The Council had asked, in its final session (1563-1565), that the Pope, assisted by a special commission, should draw up revised liturgical books to avoid 'abuses'. The resulting liturgical books were henceforth obligatory.

The Council thought it was offering books that corresponded to 'the norms of the Fathers of the Church and the ancient rites', but in fact, the post-Trent liturgy was a tidied up version of liturgy of the Roman curia.

So it remained, until the Second Vatican Council was able to reap the harvest of the work of the liturgical movement which had been growing, principally in France and Germany, since the beginning of the twentieth century.

Underlying the rich diversity that the liturgy of the Eucharist has known throughout the centuries is one simple truth: the Church has celebrated, does celebrate, and will continue to celebrate the Eucharist in faithfulness to the command given by Jesus: 'Do this in memory of me'. Throughout the ages, across continents and cultures, the central tradition continues unbroken: this is what we received; this is what, in turn, we pass on.

THE EUCHARIST TODAY OUTLINE

INTRODUCTORY RITES
  Entry song
  Sign of the cross
  Penitential rite
  [Gloria]
  Opening prayer or Collect
LITURGY OF THE WORD
  First reading
  Responsorial psalm
  [Second reading]
  Gospel acclamation
  Gospel
  Homily
  Creed
  Prayer of the Faithful
LITURGY OF THE EUCHARIST
  Preparation of the altar and the gifts
  Eucharistic prayer
  Communion rite
    Lord's Prayer
    Sign of peace
    Breaking of the bread
    Communion
CONCLUDING RITE
  Blessing
  Dismissal

INTRODUCTORY RITES

The purpose of all the rites in this opening section is to form the people who have gathered into an assembly. There is a sense in which the Sunday celebration begins from the moment each of us sets out from home to come to celebrate. But the liturgy is not celebrated by a gathering of individuals, it is celebrated by the Church, the body of Christ. Our unity will never be perfect in this world, but as we gather, we shape ourselves, as best we can, into one community, to be a sacrament of the one body of Christ.

> ***Where two or three meet***
> ***in my name,***
> ***I shall be there with them.***
> (Matthew 18:20)

Opening song

One very good way to gel a crowd into an assembly is to get them to do something together: this is part of the purpose of the entry song. Of course, normally the words of the song are already helping to focus our minds on the theme of the day's celebration, but the very fact of singing together is in itself community-building. This means it should be a song in which everyone can actually participate.

As the song is drawing to its close, the assembly finally takes shape with the procession of the celebrant and his assistants.

Sign of the cross and greeting

The assembly has gathered in God's name, in answer to his call, to celebrate Christ's paschal mystery, and in the power of the Spirit. The opening gesture of the sign of the cross, which all make together, is a reminder of:

– the Trinity

– the cross, by which Christ enters the paschal mystery

– our baptism, which makes of us the priestly people.

The celebrant then greets the assembly, in simple words, taken from the New Testament, which invoke the presence of Christ among us:

*The grace of our Lord Jesus Christ
and the love of God
and the fellowship of the Holy Spirit
be with you.*
(Taken from 2 Corinthians 13:13)

*The grace and peace of God our
Father
and the Lord Jesus Christ be with you.*
(Taken from Galatians 1:3)

The Lord be with you.
(Taken from 2 Thessalonians 3:16;
see also 2 Timothy 4:22)

Peace be with you.
(Taken from John 20:19; see also
John 20:21, 27)

Once he has evoked the presence of Christ, the celebrant then greets the assembly briefly, in his own words, in a way that helps lead them into the day's celebration.

Penitential rite

The very beginning of Christ's preaching was to invite us to 'repent, and believe the good news'.

The Church offers a moment at the beginning of the celebration where each of us individually and as a community acknowledges that we are sinners in the sight of God, and we pray for his merciful forgiveness.

This rite can take several forms:

– a general confession of sins
(the 'We confess')

– a penitential litany or dialogue

– a simple prayer for God's mercy

– blessing and sprinkling with water, as a reminder of our original forgiveness granted in baptism.

All four forms conclude with the celebrant invoking God's pardon:

*May almighty God have mercy on us,
forgive us our sins,
and bring us to everlasting life.*

or (after the sprinkling):

*May almighty God cleanse us of our
sins,
and through the Eucharist we celebrate
make us worthy to sit at his table
in his heavenly kingdom.*

If the *Kyrie* response has not already been used in the form of penitential rite chosen, it is now used – usually sung. This is a very ancient prayer, as is clear from the fact that it is still in Greek, the ordinary language of the Christians in the earliest centuries. In using it, we are recognising that the Church stretches far beyond the community gathered in our church on this day: that it extends, in space and time, to include all those who ever were and ever will be baptised, all those who have found forgiveness in the *Kyrios* (Lord) and Christ.

Gloria

If, as children of God, we turn to God in forgiveness, it is because we are already confident of that loving forgiveness. So the natural Christian response to the moment of pardon is to sing the praises of God the Father, and Christ, his Son.

This hymn, which began in the Eastern Church and which was first used as an Easter hymn and sung at the communion, opens with the Christmas song of the angels:

*Glory to God in the highest
and peace to his people on earth.*

It is a song, then, that celebrates the presence of the Lord, which we now use just before that presence among us in the Word.

Opening prayer

This is a deceptively simple part of the liturgy, to which there are in fact four moments:

– the celebrant invites all to pray

– there is a moment of silence, during which we each formulate our personal prayer to the Father

– the celebrant then gathers or 'collects' these individual and secret prayers into the prayer of the Church. This prayer celebrates some aspect of the mystery of God for which we thank him, and then moves on to ask for our ongoing needs. This is always addressed to the Father through the Son.

– finally the people ratify what the celebrant has said on their behalf by their 'Amen'.

LITURGY OF THE WORD

In Luke's Gospel we are offered the example of the risen Christ, who, on the very day of the resurrection accompanies the two disciples on the road toward Emmaus. Christ,

> *starting with Moses and going through
> all the prophets, explained to them
> the passages throughout scripture
> that were about himself.*
> (Luke 24:27)

It is only when this is complete that he takes bread, blesses, breaks and shares it with them. The disciples recognise him in the breaking of bread, but they say to each other, 'Did not our hearts burn within us as he explained the scriptures to us?'

The apostles understood that this was the model for their celebration: before sharing the bread and wine, the word is first shared. The very first community, baptised at Pentecost,

> *remained faithful to the teaching of
> the apostles,*

> *to the brotherhood,
> to the breaking of bread
> and to the prayers.*
> (Acts 2:42)

By 'the teaching of the apostles' Luke means what we would call the Liturgy of the Word.

The word was shared first, and shared extremely generously, if the following example of Paul was typical!

> *On the first day of the week we met to
> break bread. Paul was due to leave
> the next day, and he preached a
> sermon that went on till the middle
> of the night . . . as Paul went on
> and on a young man called
> Eutychus who was sitting on the
> window-sill grew drowsy and was
> overcome by sleep and fell to the
> ground three floors below. He was
> picked up dead. Paul went down
> and stooped to clasp the boy to him.
> 'There is no need to worry,' he said,
> 'there is still life in him.' Then he
> went back upstairs where he broke
> the bread and ate and carried on
> talking till he left at daybreak.*
> (Acts 20:7-11)

The texts from scripture which are read during the Liturgy of the Word are contained in the liturgical book known as the Lectionary. The choice of texts is not at all random, but chosen according to a carefully constructed programme, so that (as Vatican II demanded):

> *the treasures of the Bible be opened up
> more lavishly so that a richer share
> might be offered to the faithful at
> the table of God's word and a more
> representative portion of sacred
> scripture be read to the people over a
> prescribed number of years.*
> (Vatican II, Sacrosanctum Concilium 51)

That programme operates on two key principles:

• the Gospel is central to the liturgy of the word, and everything builds up to its proclamation or extends it

• each evangelist is given the time and space to present Christ to us in his way.

The first principle is respected by the

way the Liturgy of the Word is constructed. As it appears here, with its elements simply listed in the sections that follow, the Liturgy of the Word may seem rather linear: one item simply following another. In fact, the first reading is chosen to lead us towards, to prepare us for what we will hear in the Gospel; the psalm is a continuation, in dialogue form, of this theme or idea as presented in the first reading. To mark the importance of the Gospel, it is prepared by the acclamation, and the proclamation of the Gospel itself is continued by the words of explanation in the homily and it is what we have heard in the Gospel that inspires our intentions in the Prayer of the Faithful.

The second reading follows a programme of its own, so that in the course of the three years, all the letters of the New Testament will have been read. The second principle is respected by the three-year cycle, dedicated in turn to the Gospels of Matthew, Mark and Luke. Sadly, the shorthand way of referring to this is to talk impersonally about year A, B and C. How much better it would be if we could manage to refer to them as the Year of Matthew, the Year of Mark and the Year of Luke. John is not forgotten, but the particular paschal nature of his Gospel is respected by entrusting the season of Lent and of Easter to John. This, principally, is when we hear his Gospel. In the year of Mark, the Church supplements Mark's rather short and cryptic presentation of the multiplication of the loaves by offering John's account and the discourse on 'the bread of life' (spread across five Sundays).

First reading
(Old Testament Reading)

Though we are the people of the new covenant, Christ told us that he did not come to abolish the old but to fulfil it. We respect and honour the Old Testament as the Word of God, and look to it to enrich our understanding of the Gospel founded on and the fulfilment of the Old Testament.

As a sign that it is the Word of God, this reading is proclaimed from the ambo – that is, the lectern which is reserved for the Word of God.

In paschal time, the first reading is taken from the Acts of the Apostles, which means all three readings are from the New Testament: this is to signify that with Christ's resurrection we are living in the time of the new People of God.

Responsorial psalm

In all the scriptures God addresses his word to us, calling us to respond. The Liturgy of the Word offers this symbolic moment when God's people respond, using words from sacred scripture. This is usually a poem or a canticle from the Psalms though occasionally it may be a canticle from one of the Old Testament prophets. In either case, the original literary form is a song, which means that normally it should be sung!

The response suggested by the Lectionary often gives or hints at the Christian rereading of the psalm, interpreting it on the lips of Christ or as the voice of the Church.

Second reading
(New Testament Reading)

In the Creed we declare that we believe in a Church which is 'apostolic'. Here, Sunday by Sunday, is a very concrete expression of that. The voice of Paul, Peter, John and James, or of the author of the Letter to the Hebrews is heard in our midst, continuing their apostolic teaching, guiding the Church now as they did in their lifetimes.

The totality of the apostolic teaching is presented across the three-year cycle. Unfortunately, this does mean that there is not always a complete or evident coherence between the content of the second reading and that of the Gospel.

Gospel acclamation

We are approaching the summit of the Liturgy of the Word, which is symbolised by a whole series of gestures. Until now we have been sitting; now we stand, as a mark of respect. The Book of the Gospels is carried in procession, accompanied by candles and incense. Meantime, the whole assembly proclaims the presence of Christ among us in the Gospel by singing the 'Alleluia'. (In Lent, this great shout of praise is muted a little; but still we acclaim 'Glory and praise to you, O Christ!')

Gospel

'In the liturgy, God is still talking to his people, Christ is still proclaiming his Gospel.' (Vatican II, Sacrosanctum Concilium 33.) The Gospel is proclaimed, not as something past, but as present and dynamic:

Jesus began to speak,
'This text is being fulfilled today
even as you listen'
(Luke 4:21)

As a mark of respect for the presence of Christ, only an ordained minister may proclaim the Gospel. (However, this is a ministerial service, not a presidential service, so, where there is more than one priest-celebrant, it is better if the Gospel is proclaimed by a minister other than the celebrant.) The minister prepares himself for proclaiming the Gospel by a blessing:

The Lord be in your heart and on
your lips
that you may worthily proclaim his
gospel.

or a prayer:
Almighty God,
cleanse my heart and my lips
that I may worthily proclaim your
gospel.

Homily

The homily is an integral part of the liturgy of the word, and its purpose is to explore the readings of the day, especially the Gospel, so that their message becomes clearer for that particular community in that particular place and at that particular time. It is a moment for the Word to become incarnate in the here and now of the celebating community.

Creed

The historical purpose of the Creed at this point in the celebration was to distinguish those who were not yet baptised, the catechumens and the elect who shared in the Liturgy of the Word, but who could not yet share in the liturgy reserved for 'the faithful' (that is, the baptised).

In most Sunday celebrations nowadays the Creed offers the people

the opportunity to respond and give
assent to the word of God which
they have heard in the readings and
the homily.
(The General Instruction on the Roman Missal, 43)

It should also serve as a reminder that if we participate in the Eucharist, it is as a priestly people, consecrated by our baptism: in the Creed we are renewing our baptismal profession of faith before cele brating the Eucharist.

The Missal contains two ancient Creeds: the shorter, older one, known as the Apostles' Creed. The preferred form of the Creed for normal Sunday use is the longer Nicene Creed.

Prayer of the Faithful

The Prayer of the Faithful acts like a hinge between the Liturgy of the Word and the Liturgy of the Eucharist.

It is the concluding moment of the Liturgy of the Word, in which, having heard the demands of the Gospel, we pray to God for strength to live them out. The Gospel is Good News, as Church we are charged with the mission of bringing this Good News to the world, hence this great prayer for ourselves as Church, and for the world, which as Church, we have to serve.

The prayer is built on a fourfold structure:

– an invitation to pray by the celebrant

– a series of intentions proposed to the assembly by the deacon or by a reader

– after a moment of silent prayer, the people reply by a prayer or acclamation of supplication

– the celebrant gathers all the supplications into a concluding prayer, which is ratified by the people's 'Amen'.

The Roman Missal offers not only examples of the prayer, from introduction through intentions to conclusion, but also very clear guidelines as to the content and sequence of the intentions:

THE FOURFOLD STRUCTURE OF THE EUCHARIST

AT THE LAST SUPPER

Paul's First Letter to the Corinthians and the three synoptic Gospels clearly express the simple but fundamental fourfold structure of the Eucharist:

1 Jesus *took* bread
Matt 26:26; Mk 14:22; Lk 22:19; 1 Cor 11:23

2a He *blessed* it
Matt 26:26; Mk 14:22

2b He *gave thanks*
Lk 22:19; 1 Cor 11:24

3 He *broke* it
Matt 26:26; Mk 14:22; Lk 22:19; 1 Cor 11:23

4 He *gave* it
Matt 26:26; Mk 14:22; Lk 22:19; cf 1 Cor 11:26

IN THE NARRATIVES OF FEEDING THE CROWDS

We find this same structure present in the accounts of what is sometimes known as 'the multiplication of the loaves' or 'the miracle of the loaves'.

These accounts are found in the Synoptic Gospels as follows:

First miracle of the loaves

Matthew 14:13-21
Jesus *took* . . . *said the blessing*; *breaking* the loaves he handed them to the disciples who *gave* them to the crowds.

Mark 6:30-44
Jesus *took* . . . *said the blessing*; then he *broke* the loaves and handed them to his disciples to *distribute* among the people.

Luke 9:10-17
Jesus *took* the loaves . . . *said the blessing* over them; then he *broke* them and handed them to the disciples to *distribute* among the crowd.

Second miracle of the loaves

Matthew 15:32-39
Jesus *took*... and he *gave thanks* and *broke* them and handed them to the disciples who *gave* them to the crowds.

Mark 8:1-10
Jesus *took* the seven loaves, and *after giving thanks* he *broke* them and handed them to his disciples to *distribute*.

- for the needs of the Church
- for public authorities and for the salvation of the world
- for those oppressed by any need
- for the local community.

(The General Instruction on the Roman Missal, 45-46)

LITURGY OF THE EUCHARIST

The celebrant now moves to the altar, which is the table of the Lord, at which the Church, Christ's body, renews the meal he shared with his disciples the night before he died; at which the Church recognises the presence of the risen Lord in the breaking of bread, as experienced by the disciples on the day of the resurrection (Luke 24:30-31); and in which the Church looks forward to sharing in the banquet feast of the Lamb (Apocalypse 7:16).

Until now present in the assembly and present in the priest, the Body of Christ, head and members now makes Christ present under the sacramental signs of bread and wine.

The Eucharist is structured around the fourfold action so clearly given in the Gospels and by Paul (see left):

the Lord Jesus **took** some bread,
and **thanked God** for it
and **broke** it
and **gave** it.

So now the Church
takes bread (the preparation of the gifts)
thanks God for it (eucharistic prayer)
breaks it (fraction)
and **gives** it (communion).

Preparation of the altar and of the gifts

The bread and wine which are needed in order to celebrate the Lord's supper are now brought to the altar. Ideally, these gifts should come from the assembly, and, as a sign of this they are brought forward and presented by members of the congregation.

It is no longer the custom, as it was in the early Church, for people to bring bread

and wine from their homes to present: instead, they now bring money or gifts for the poor or for the Church.

It would be better to avoid describing this part of the Mass as 'offertory', because there is a risk that this be confused with 'offering'; the moment of offering comes later, in the eucharistic prayer. Here the gifts are simply presented to the celebrant, who receives them, acknowledging them, in the words of the traditional Jewish grace, as gifts of God the Creator and fruit of human work:

Blessed are you, Lord, God of all creation.
Through your goodness we have this bread to offer,
which earth has given and human hands have made.
It will become for us the bread of life.

Similarly for the wine, which
. . . will become our spiritual drink.

To both, the assembly reply . . .
Blessed be God for ever.

The fact that these prayers are Jewish in origin, and that something very similar would have been said by Jesus, makes a tangibly symbolic link between us and Christ who commands us to celebrate the Eucharist.

This moment of 'taking' the bread and wine concludes with a prayer, which indicates quite clearly the purpose of these gifts: it is in order that we have

. . . a sacrifice
that may be acceptable to God the almighty Father.

And the people reply, reaffirming the purpose of the sacrifice which is to follow . . .

. . . for the praise and glory of God's name,
for our good,
and the good of all the Church.

Eucharistic prayer

'Eucharist' is derived from a Greek verb, meaning 'to give thanks'. The entire prayer is a prayer of blessing and thanksgiving, though we can distinguish various movements within this great act of thanksgiving.

Nowadays, the Missal offers a variety of eucharistic prayers (see right). All are basically inspired by the words uttered by Jesus over the bread and wine in the course of his Last Supper on the night before he died.

The Gospels give only the essential description, and none of them offers the exact full prayer that Christ said. However, the Old and New Testament offer numerous examples of prayers and songs of thanksgiving and of blessing.

The eucharistic prayer is also the great prayer of Christ offering himself to the Father 'so that sins may be forgiven'. It is the priestly prayer, par excellence. It is for this reason that the Eucharist can only be celebrated by an assembly together with someone who has received the laying on of hands for this ministry: that is to say, a priest or a bishop. This is the prayer of Christ: therefore, the body of Christ must be represented, head and members. This important interplay between the priestly people and the ordained minister is symbolised above all by the introductory dialogue and the final great Amen, as well as by the other key moments when the assembly actively express an acclamation. Moreover, the priest prays the prayer saying 'We praise . . . we offer'. He speaks not in his own name, but on behalf of the Church:

the priest unites the people with
  himself
in the prayer he addresses
in their name to the Father
through Jesus Christ.

(General Instruction on the Roman Missal, 54)

The elements in the eucharistic prayer are:

  introductory dialogue
  thanksgiving
  acclamation
  epiclesis, or invocation of the Holy
    Spirit
  narrative of consecration and words of
    institution
  anamnesis or 'making memory'
  offering
  intercessions
  final doxology

The best way to explore these elements is by examining specific examples from the various eucharistic prayers.

The introductory dialogue exists to constitute one single assembly, priest and people, united in acknowledging with thanksgiving the works of God and in offering him sacrifice:

The Lord be with you.
And also with you.

All that follows is done because it was expressly commanded by Christ himself; if we are able to do it, it is because the Lord is indeed 'with us'.

Lift up your hearts.
We lift them up to the Lord.

Together, priest and people embark on a great act of offering: beyond the visible gifts, it is ourselves that we offer, in imitation of Christ, indeed, as Christ's body.

Let us give thanks to the Lord our
  God.
It is right to give him thanks and
  praise.

The dialogue ends on a note that sets the tone for what will follow: we offer ourselves, but above all we offer in *thanksgiving*, we make *eucharist*.

Thanks and praise is then voiced by the priest, on behalf of all, above all in the preface. The preface begins (taking up the last words the assembly said)

Father, all powerful and ever-living
  God,
we do well
always and everywhere
to give you thanks . . .

One of the particular charisms of the Roman Rite is that is has always (even when it had only one eucharistic prayer) had a great variety of prefaces, prayers of praise to the Father for a particular aspect of the work of salvation. This means that our thanksgiving can take on a very particular colour, according to the season, the feast, or the event that is being celebrated.

Here is an extract from a preface for ordinary time, which gives thanks for creation:

All things are of your making,
all times and seasons obey your laws,
but you chose to create man in your
  own image,
setting him over the whole world in all

THE EUCHARISTIC PRAYER TODAY

In the Roman Missal as revised by the demand of Vatican II, there are four Eucharistic Prayers.

Eucharistic Prayer I, also known as the Roman Canon, which (with only a little simplification of certain sections which referred very specifically to local Roman saints) was the only Eucharistic Prayer in use in the West for about 10 centuries. Although de facto the one most used in the West, it only became officially uniform with the Missal of Pius V (1580).

Eucharistic Prayer II is based on elements from the document we know as the Apostolic Tradition of Hippolytus. This, then, is based on what was in use in Rome in the early-third-century.

Eucharistic Prayer III is a new composition, but based on the tradition of the Church in the broadest sense. It expresses for us today what the various traditions throughout time and across the various cultures have strived to pray. In particular, the prayer was drawn up so that the various elements which go to structure the prayer are as clear as possible.

Eucharistic Prayer IV is very largely inspired by an anaphora (the eucharistic prayer) from the Eastern liturgy of Saint Basil. Its particular characteristic is to work through the various moments throughout history when God intervened to save us, and for which we should 'give thanks'.

Subsequent to the promulgation of the Roman Missal, five other Eucharistic Prayers have been officially approved: three for use at Masses with children, two of which have additional acclamations, to help the children participate more fully in the prayer; and two for Masses of Reconciliation.

In some countries (including Great Britain), there is also a special Eucharistic Prayer for use at Masses with the deaf. The language of prayer is often complex and abstract, whereas, to be signed for the deaf, the language needs to be as simple and concrete as possible. It is the celebrant himself who should sign the text as he prays it aloud. Because it is designed as an integral whole, this prayer may never be used without it being signed.

Since 1974, Switzerland has had a Eucharistic Prayer with four variants; originally for use at their Synods, it has subsequently also been approved for other countries such as France, Italy and Spain.

THE MOVEMENT OF THE EUCHARISTIC PRAYER

The *anaphora*: with the Eucharistic Prayer (the prayer of thanksgiving and consecration) we come to the heart and summit of the celebration:

In the *preface*, the Church gives thanks to the Father, through Christ, in the Holy Spirit, for all his works: creation, redemption, and sanctification. The whole community thus joins in the unending praise that the Church in heaven, the angels and all the saints, sing to the thrice-holy God.

In the *epiclesis*, the Church asks the Father to send his Holy Spirit (or the power of his blessing [cf Eucharistic Prayer I]) on the bread and wine, so that by his power they may become the body and blood of Jesus Christ and so that those who take part in the Eucharist may be one body and one spirit (some liturgical traditions put the epiclesis after the anamnesis). In *the institution narrative*, the power of the words and the action of Christ, and the power of the Holy Spirit, make sacramentally present under the species of bread and wine Christ's body and blood, his sacrifice offered on the cross once for all.

In the *anamnesis* that follows, the Church calls to mind the Passion, resurrection, and glorious return of Christ Jesus; she presents to the Father the offering of his Son which reconciles us with him.

In the *intercessions*, the Church indicates that the Eucharist is celebrated in communion with the whole Church in heaven and on earth, the living and the dead, and in communion with the pastors of the Church, the Pope, the diocesan bishop, his presbyterium and his deacons, and all the bishops of the whole world together with their Churches.

Catechism 1352-54

its wonder.
You made man the steward of creation,
to praise you day by day
for the marvels of your wisdom and power . . .

So, the prefaces conclude, we proclaim your glory; but we do so conscious that we are not the first nor will we be the last to appreciate these wonders, which is why we add something like

. . . so, with the angels and saints in heaven
we proclaim your glory
and join in their unending hymn of praise . . .

Acclamation. This initial moment of thanksgiving comes to a climactic conclusion with the whole assembly singing:

Holy, holy, holy Lord God of power and might,
heaven and earth are full of your glory.
Hosanna in the highest.
Blessed is he who comes in the name of the Lord.
Hosanna in the highest.

The thanksgiving continues, but after the Holy, holy, its focus narrows to offer thanks for the work of Christ, especially in his work as mediator:

Father, you are holy indeed,
and all creation rightly gives you praise.
All life, all holiness comes from you
through your Son, Jesus Christ our Lord,
by the working of the Holy Spirit.
From age to age you gather a people to yourself,
so that from east to west
a perfect offering may be made
to the glory of your name.
(Eucharistic Prayer III)

Epiclesis, borrowed from the Greek, is a technical word which means a prayer of **invocation of the Holy Spirit**. At this point in the eucharistic prayer, explicit mention is made of the gifts of bread and wine, the offerings, and the Holy Spirit is invoked that he may come upon them, and make them holy:

Let your Spirit come upon these gifts to make them holy,

so that they may become for us
the body and blood of our Lord Jesus Christ.
(Eucharistic Prayer II)

The prayer now moves very naturally to the narrative institution, the account of Jesus taking bread and wine at the Last Supper:

He always loved those who were his own in the world.
When the time came for him to be glorified by you,
his heavenly Father,
he showed the depth of his love.
While they were at supper,
he took bread, said the blessing, broke the bread,
and gave it to his disciples . . .

and includes his words over the bread and wine, which are the **words of consecration**, common to all the eucharistic prayers. First, over the bread:

Take this, all of you and eat it:
this is my body which will be given up for you.

Then, over the cup of wine:

Take this, all of you, and drink from it:
this is the cup of my blood,
the blood of the new and everlasting covenant.
It will be shed for you and for all
so that sins may be forgiven.

And the words of Christ, said in every eucharistic prayer, include this command:

Do this in memory of me.

That command is immediately fulfilled, as the assembly makes a proclamation of faith which is 'in memory' of Christ. For us, **making memory** is usually limited to recalling events from the past. For the Semitic peoples, making memory means calling up everything that is not in the present and making it present. 'Making memory' means making present past and future: hence the threefold structure of all of the memorial acclamations, proclaiming the three stages of the paschal mystery: Christ's death (in the past, once and for all); Christ's resurrection (the risen Christ is present); his glorification (which has begun already, but will only be completely fulfilled at the end of time):

Christ has died
Christ is risen
Christ will come again.

The technical name for this 'making memory' is another word borrowed from the Greek: **anamnesis.**

The priest takes up the people's memorial acclamation, past, present and looking to the future, as he prays:

Father, we now celebrate this
  memorial of our redemption.
We recall Christ's death,
  his descent among the dead,
his resurrection
  and his ascension to your right
  hand;
and, looking forward to your coming
  in your glory . . .
(Eucharistic Prayer IV)

Here the prayer moves seamlessly from one aspect to another; while still making memory, the prayer becomes explicitly one of **offering:**

and, looking forward to your coming
  in your glory,
we offer you his body and blood,
the acceptable sacrifice
which brings salvation to the whole
  world.
(Eucharistic Prayer IV)

. . . ready to greet him when he comes
  again,
we offer you in thanksgiving this holy
  and living sacrifice.

Look with favour on your Church's
  offering,
and see the Victim whose death has
  reconciled us to yourself.
(Eucharistic Prayer III)

. . . from the many gifts you have
  given us

we offer to you, God of glory and
  majesty,
the holy and perfect sacrifice:
the bread of life
and the cup of eternal salvation.
(Eucharistic Prayer I)

The Roman Missal, explicitly echoing Vatican II's *Constitution on the Sacred Liturgy (no 48)*, explains:

> **'In this memorial,**
> **the Church – and in particular the**
> **Church here and now assembled –**
> **offers the victim to the Father**
> **in the Holy Spirit.**
> **The church's intention is**
> **that the faithful not only offer**
> **the spotless victim**
> **but also learn to offer themselves**
> **and daily to be drawn**
> **into ever more perfect union,**
> **through Christ the Mediator,**
> **with the Father**
> **and with each other,**
> **so that at last**
> **God may be all in all . . .**
>
> *(The General Instruction*
> *on the Roman Missal 55F)*

This identification of offering ourselves with Christ works through our 'incorporation' into Christ, our joining Christ in his body: this has begun in baptism, is strengthened in confirmation – but always, by the power of the Spirit. Here, in the eucharistic prayer, the Church again **invokes the Holy Spirit,** again so that Christ's body and blood may be truly present: but this time, it is that Christ be present in and through us:

Grant that we who are nourished by
  his body and blood,
may be filled with the Holy Spirit,
and become one body, one spirit in
  Christ.
(Eucharistic Prayer III)

. . . by your Holy Spirit,
gather all who share this bread and
  wine
into the one body of Christ,

a living sacrifice of praise.
(Eucharistic Prayer IV)

Christ's sacrifice was made for all, and therefore, having recalled his perfect offering, the Church dares to place before God intercessions for the living and for the dead. These **intercessions** go way beyond those gathered together for the celebration, to include the whole Church, and even wider to 'all God's children', to all who seek God 'with a sincere heart'. A universal prayer indeed:

For the living

Lord, may this sacrifice which has made our peace with you,
advance the peace and salvation of all the world.
Strengthen in love your pilgrim Church on earth;
your servant, Pope ......,
our bishop ......
and all the bishops,
with the clergy and the entire people your Son has gained for you.
Father, hear the prayers of the family you have gathered here before you.
In mercy and love unite all your children,
wherever they may be.
(Eucharistic Prayer III)

Remember those who take part in this offering,
those here present and all your people,
and all who seek you with a sincere heart.
(Eucharistic Prayer IV)

For the dead

Remember, Lord, those who have died and have gone before us marked with the sign of faith,
especially those for whom we now pray,
......[they are mentioned by name]
May these, and all who sleep in Christ, find in your presence
light, happiness and peace.
(Eucharistic Prayer I)

Remember those who died in the peace of Christ,
and all the dead whose faith is known to you alone.
(Eucharistic Prayer IV)

It is at this point in the eucharistic prayer that, whenever the Eucharist has been preceded by another sacrament, special mention can be made of those who received that sacrament: baptism, confirmation, anointing, marriage, ordination. Examples of this are given in the relevant chapters.

Thinking of those already dead directs the prayer to the end of time when

. . . we shall see you, our God, as you are.
(Eucharistic Prayer III)

and when the praise and thanksgiving we shall be able to offer will be perfect.

So the prayer comes to a magnificent conclusion; as the priest raises the bread and wine in a solemn gesture of offering, he utters the great doxology, the praise of God, Father, Son and Spirit:

Through him (i.e.Christ),
with him,
in him
in the unity of the Holy Spirit,
all glory and honour is yours, almighty Father,
for ever and ever.

And then should sound what Saint Jerome described as 'a thunderclap', the great Amen by which the assembly ratifies all that has been said and done in their name.

Communion rite

The whole of the communion rite is designed to enable us to respond – but to respond properly – to Christ's invitation:

'Take, eat ... Take, drink...'

Our Father

First we say the prayer that Christ himself gave us, the prayer which is that of the children of God, that is, the baptised. We dare to address God as Father.

There are two requests that Jesus teaches us to make of God our Father: to ask for 'our daily bread' and to ask forgiveness.

When said at Mass, the last petition is developed by an additional prayer in which the priest, in the name of the community, begs deliverance from the power of evil.

Sign of peace

Forgiveness, Jesus warns in Matthew's Gospel, should be sought before coming to the table of the Lord:

If you are bringing your offering to the altar
and there remember
that your brother has something against you,
leave your offering there before the altar,
go and be reconciled with your brother first,
and then come back and present your offering.
(Matthew 5:23-24)

So it is that the whole assembly shares a sign of peace. 'Before sharing the same bread, the people express their love for one another and beg for peace and unity in the Church and with all humankind.' (General Instruction on the Roman Missal, 56b)

Breaking the Bread

The oldest name given to the celebration of the Eucharist was 'the breaking of bread' (cf. Acts 2:42, 46).

Beyond the practical necessity of having to divide the bread so that it can be shared in communion, this is a very evocative symbolic gesture. Not only does it symbolise Christ being broken for many, but also that we who are many are made one body in the one bread of life which is Christ (cf. 1 Corinthians 10:17).

This gesture is considered so eloquent that it is made without any words on the part of the priest. The assembly say or sing the Lamb of God while the breaking takes place, and the singing should last as long 'as necessary to accompany the breaking of the bread'.

> *Just as this broken bread*
> *was first scattered on the hills,*
> *and was gathered up again,*
> *into one,*
> *so may your Church be gathered*
> *from the ends of the earth*
> *into your Kingdom . . .*
>
> *Didaché 9:5*
> *(late-first- early-second-century)*

Communion

It is in taking up the theme of their song that the priest invites the assembly to communion:

This is the Lamb of God
who takes away the sin of the world.
Happy are those who are called to his supper.

To which the people respond in words borrowed from the centurion in the Gospel (cf. Luke 7:1-10, especially verses 6-7):

Lord, I am not worthy to receive you, but only say the word and I shall be healed.

The Roman Missal says:

The sign of communion is more complete when given under both kinds, since the sign of the eucharistic meal appears more clearly.

Certainly, the communion offered to the assembly should be:

'in hosts consecrated at that same Mass.' (The General Instruction on the Roman Missal 56h)

At communion, those who have been washed in the blood of the Lamb are invited to feast at his table. To make it a festive moment, then, an appropriate song should accompany the communion procession.

But above all, the way in which the assembly advance to and return from the table should be calm and orderly, expressing the idea of one family in Christ sharing at the same table. There is no point in having exchanged a sign of peace if people now trample each other to get to communion!

After communion, priest and people may spend some time in silent prayer. If desired, a hymn, psalm, or other song of praise may be sung by

THE TITLES GIVEN TO THIS SACRAMENT

Nowadays, it is usual to speak of the celebration of 'the Eucharist'; a couple of generations ago, they talked almost exclusively of 'Mass'; in the Acts of the Apostles Luke speaks of 'the breaking of the bread'; Paul insists on the 'memorial'.

This central sacrament has had many titles throughout the centuries and across the various cultures of the world.

Here is how they are summarised by the Catechism.

The inexhaustible richness of this sacrament is expressed in the different names we give it. Each name evokes certain aspects of it.

It is called:

Eucharist, because it is an action of thanksgiving to God. The Greek words *eucharistein* [Lk 22:19; 1 Cor 11:24] and *eulogein* [Matt 26:26; Mk 14:22] recall the Jewish blessings that proclaim – especially during a meal – God's works: creation, redemption, and sanctification.

The Lord's Supper [cf. 1 Cor 11:20], because of its connection with *the supper* which the Lord took with his disciples on the eve of his Passion and because it anticipates *the wedding feast of the Lamb* in the heavenly Jerusalem [cf. Apoc 19:9].

The Breaking of Bread, because Jesus used this rite, part of a Jewish meal, when as master of the table he blessed and distributed the bread [Matt 14:19, 15:36; Mk 8:6,19], above all at the Last Supper [Matt 26:26; 1 Cor 11:14]. It is by this action that his disciples will recognize him after his Resurrection [Lk 24:13-35], and it is this expression that the first Christians will use to designate their Eucharistic assemblies [Acts 2:42, 46, 20:7,11]; by doing so they signified that all who eat the one broken bread, Christ, enter into communion with him and form but one body in him [1 Cor 10:16-17].

The Eucharistic Assembly (*synaxis*), because the Eucharist is celebrated amid the assembly of the faithful, the visible expression of the Church [1 Cor 11:17-34].

1330 The memorial of the Lord's Passion and Resurrection.

The Holy Sacrifice, because it makes present the one sacrifice of Christ the Saviour and includes the Church's offering. The terms *holy sacrifice of the Mass*, 'sacrifice of praise' [Heb 13:15, cf. Ps 116:13, 17], *spiritual sacrifice* [1 Pet 2:5], *pure and holy sacrifice* are also used [Mal 1:11], since it completes and surpasses all the sacrifices of the old covenant.

The Holy and Divine Liturgy, because the Church's whole liturgy finds its center and most intense expression in the celebration of this sacrament; in the same sense we also call its celebration *the Sacred Mysteries*. We speak of the *Most Blessed Sacrament* because it is the Sacrament of sacraments. The eucharistic species reserved in the tabernacle are designated by this same name.

Holy Communion, because by this sacrament we unite ourselves to Christ, who makes us sharers in his Body and Blood to form a single body [1 Cor 10:16-17]. We also call it: *the holy things* (*ta hagia; sancta*) [Apostolic Constitutions 8:13, 12; Didaché 9:5, 10:6] – the first meaning of the phrase 'communion of saints' in the Apostles' Creed – the *bread of angels, bread from heaven, medicine of immortality* [Ignatius of Antioch, Eph 20:2], viaticum . . .

Holy Mass (*Missa*), because the liturgy in which the mystery of salvation is accomplished concludes with the sending forth (*mission*) of the faithful, so that they may fulfil God's will in their daily lives.

Catechism 1328-1332

the entire congregation.
(The General Instruction on the Roman Missal 56j)

Prayer after communion

The priest addresses one last prayer to the Father in the name of the community, asking God that what has been celebrated in sign and symbols may become reality, that the Eucharist may bear fruit in the lives of each member of the assembly, and in the life of the community:

Father,
you increase our faith and hope,
you deepen our love in communion.
Help us to live by your words
and to seek Christ, our bread of life...
(1st Sunday of Lent)

Lord,
you renew us at your table with the
*   bread of life.*
May this food strengthen us in love
and help us to serve you in each other.
(22nd Sunday in Ordinary Time)

CONCLUDING RITES
Blessing

The priest offers the people God's blessing, which may be in the simple form:

May almighty God bless you,
the Father and the Son and the Holy
Spirit.

The Roman Missal offers a whole range of solemn blessings, that is to say usually a triple form of invocation which precede the final blessing formula. For example, in Ordinary Time, the following, based on the traditional blessing of Aaron (cf. Numbers 6:24-26),can be used:

May the Lord bless you and keep you.
Amen.
May his face shine upon you,
and be gracious to you.
Amen.
May he look upon you with kindness,
and give you his peace.
Amen.

In addition to the solemn blessings offered by the Roman Missal, for Masses during which another sacrament has been celebrated, the various rituals offer appropriate solemn blessings. Examples are given in the relevant chapters.

Dismissal

We have already noted how the oldest 'nickname' for the celebration of the Eucharist was 'the breaking of bread'. The shorthand name that is most current nowadays is 'the Mass', which is derived from '*missa*' which was one of the very last words that the celebrant said to the assembly. In Latin this used to be: *Ite, missa est*. Today's vernacular equivalent is:

Go in the peace of Christ.
or
The Mass is ended, go in peace.
or
Go in peace to love and serve the Lord.

The Roman Missal sees the dismissal as each member of the congregation 'being sent to do good works, praising and blessing the Lord' (The General Instruction on the Roman Missal, 57b.)

In calling the celebration 'Mass' we are affirming that what is celebrated within the confines of the Church building is only the beginning: that strengthened by the Eucharist we go out, we are 'sent' to continue Christ's work in the power of the Spirit of bringing all to God the Father.

RECONCILIATION
Come back to me . . .

SAYING SORRY

Some years ago a very popular film was advertised by the slogan 'Love means never having to say sorry'. A very clever slogan, because it appeals to how we would like love to be – and all the more appealing because it is not always how things work out in fact!

If we really loved someone, then we would never do anything to hurt that person, and so there would be no occasion when we would have to say sorry. That is the ideal. In fact, love is a very complex emotion, and it can wax and wane. We may love someone very much, but within all of us there is the fundamental instinct of self-love. Even in our love of others, self-love is at work, to a greater or lesser extent.

Sometimes this self-love can cause us to say and do things which hurt other people, even those we love. We ourselves can feel hurt by the person we love and we may respond in a way which then causes them hurt.

Love can – and does – mean having to say sorry. When these moments of hurt do take place, if we behaved as if nothing had happened, if we ignore the hurt, just think what additional harm we might do! We would be damaging the relationship even more, perhaps even destroying it. Both partners in the relationship would suffer, would be hurt and damaged.

Never saying sorry means never 'repairing' relationships that have been damaged. It means not making good the hurt – including the hurt we ourselves feel. Never saying sorry would lead us to become more self-centred and eventually we may lose the capacity to love anyone but ourselves.

When a relationship is damaged, the first step in repairing the harm is to admit where the failure has been, and make apology for it. If we can find the courage and

the love to do that, there can be a fresh start, the relationship can be restored, can progress and deepen.

Why should saying sorry be so difficult? Perhaps we are afraid that our apology will be rejected. Perhaps we are afraid that the other person may be too hurt and that saying sorry will only make things worse. Often, we have to admit, it is quite simply because we do not like admitting we are wrong.

So saying sorry may be difficult because we are afraid:
– afraid of rejection
– afraid of humiliation
– afraid of recognising and accepting ourselves as we are.

These fears are signs that our love is not yet perfect. More importantly, love will overcome these difficulties:

In love there can be no fear,
but fear is driven out by perfect love.
(1 John 4:18)

Saying sorry is already a sign of working toward this love. Our apology is a sign that we want our love to grow so that it will help us overcome our fears and hesitations.

The slogan ought to be 'Love is knowing how to say sorry – and mean it!' If our love is genuine, we will want to heal any damage we may have caused to that relationship, wanting to tell the person we have hurt that we really do love and care. 'Saying sorry' is an essential part of a growing, healthy relationship of love.

OUR RELATIONSHIP WITH GOD

When God created us, he chose to enter into a relationship with us. The relationship begins at his initiative, an initiative of love. But, of course, a relationship is not just one-way: the only adequate response for love received

THE NAME OF THIS SACRAMENT

Throughout history, the way in which this sacrament has been celebrated has evolved considerably, and it has had different titles, depending on which of its features was predominant. Immediately before Vatican II, for example, the commonest name was 'confession'; in the early Church, when it was seen as parallel to baptism, it was referred to as 'conversion'. Vatican II preferred the traditional title of 'penance', to underline the fact that the sacrament should just be one moment in a lifelong attitude of turning toward God.

*Here is how the **Catechism** presents the various titles:*

It is called the **sacrament of conversion** because it makes sacramentally present Jesus' call to conversion (Mark 1:15), the first step in returning to the Father (cf. Luke 15:18) from whom one has strayed by sin.

It is called the **sacrament of penance**, since it consecrates the Christian sinner's personal and ecclesial steps of conversion, penance, and satisfaction.

It is called the **sacrament of confession**, since the disclosure of sins to a priest is an essential element of this sacrament. In a profound sense it is also a 'confession' (acknowledgement and praise) of the holiness of God and of his mercy toward sinful man.

It is called the **sacrament of forgiveness**, since by the priest's sacramental absolution God grants the penitent 'pardon and peace' (cf. the words of absolution).

It is call the **sacrament of reconciliation**, because it imparts to the sinner the love of God who reconciles: 'Be reconciled to God' (2 Corinthians 5:20). He who lives by God's merciful love is ready to respond to the Lord's call: 'Go; first be reconciled to your brother' (Matthew 5.24).

(Catechism 1423-1424)

from God is to offer him our love in return. But precisely because it is a relationship of love, God respects our freedom, does not oblige us, does not force us to love him in return.

The Bible uses two metaphors, two very real human images, to describe the relationship between Creator and creature, between God and us.

One image is that of a parent (sometimes father, sometimes mother) and a child:

> *When Israel was a child*
> *I loved him,*
> *and I called my son out of Egypt.*
> *But the more I called him,*
> *the further he went from me;*
> . . .
> *I myself taught Ephraim to walk,*
> *I took him in my arms;*
> *yet he has not understood*
> *that I was the one looking after him,*
> *I was like someone*
> *who lifts an infant*
> *close against his cheek;*
> *stooping down to give him his food.*
>
> (Hosea 11:1-6)

A second image is the relationship of a married couple, of man and wife:

> *Do not be afraid,*
> *you will not be put to shame,*
> *do not be dismayed,*
> *you will not be disgraced;*
> . . .
> *For now your Creator*
> *will be your husband.*
> *Yes, like a forsaken wife,*
> *distressed in spirit,*
> *the Lord calls you back.*
>
> (Isaiah 54:4-6)

These images are not cosy, ideal ones. In both there is more than a hint that the relationship is far from perfect from the human partner's point of view. But equally we ought to notice how strongly these texts express a sense of longing on the part of God to share the relationship with us.

The two images chosen use the deepest, most intense forms of human personal relationships: parent and child, man and wife.

Yet even these are only images, pale images, a mere shadow of the love that God has for us and which he invites us to share with him.

God – who is love – calls out in love to us, hoping for love in return. And how have we responded?

The biblical way of confronting this question is to offer a set-piece, namely that of Adam and Eve in the Garden of Eden (Genesis 2 and 3). Adam and Eve are, of course, symbolic characters, standing for all of us and our relationships with each other and with God. That is why this episode is placed among the very first chapters of the first book of the Bible – that is, to show that what is depicted seems to be a fundamental human characteristic.

We refer in a shorthand way to the 'Fall' – and often forget what was the starting point. Humankind's first 'home' is paradise, with God. In Genesis 2, God is pictured as fashioning 'man' *(adam)* from the dust of the soil *(adamah):* not only is there a play on the words man/soil, but more importantly Adam is in fact a collective noun. Then comes the moment pregnant with meaning: God shares his own breath, his own spirit with what he has created: God breathed into his nostrils a breath of life, and thus Adam became a living thing.

God, out of love for this living creature, sees his need of a helpmate: so, in this account, the animals are created, and presented to Adam, who gives them names. But none is suitable as a true helpmate with whom Adam can form a relationship of equals. So it is that while Adam sleeps, God takes one of his ribs, enrobes it in flesh, to make woman (another play on words). Adam is delighted, and sings the first ever love song.

So we have Adam and partner in Eden, in Paradise. This partner is as yet anonymous, but in the sense that she needs no name, so complete is the understanding and relationship between her and Adam. Both totally innocent, as the account emphasises by saying they were both 'naked but felt no shame'. There was nothing to be ashamed of, nothing for which to say sorry.

But things do not remain that way for long: first the woman and then Adam eat of the fruit of the Tree that God had forbidden. Remember this is a very symbolic set-piece: those who wrote the text and those who read it recognise themselves in these symbolic characters: we choose to go our way, not God's. We want to be in control of our own lives. How many times has this phrase been uttered down the generations, as children assert their independence of parents, of school or other institutions? Ultimately, this phrase means that we want to be in control instead of God, that we put ourselves first.

The consequence is quite the opposite: instead of asserting control over their lives, their relationships start to fall apart. This is symbolised in the story by the metaphor of hiding. Reading carefully, we find three kinds of 'hiding'.

First of all, Adam and his partner feel the need to hide themselves from each other:

> the eyes of both of them were opened,
> and they realised that they were naked.
> So they sewed fig-leaves together
> to make themselves loin-cloths.
> (Genesis 3:7)

We hide from each other: even in the best of our relationships, our basic self-interest makes us hold back, we never give ourselves completely, disinterestedly, there always remains a pocket of self-interest, of selfishness.

The second step is that they both hide from God. 'Where are you?' God asks (a very neat touch of irony, since God already knows full well not just where Adam is but what he has done). 'I was afraid,' comes the answer – and so, for lack of love, fear appears. 'I was afraid because I was naked, so I hid.' God does not arrive ready to condemn his creature; it is Adam and his partner who hide. This is a direct consequence of their having chosen to go against God's way; they set up a barrier between themselves and God.

There then comes a third and decisively fatal step: God questions Adam – at which point we can imagine that he could have admitted his mistake, could have said sorry. Instead, Adam hides even more in passing the blame onto 'the woman you put with me' and in turn, she blames the serpent.

This is the deepest form of 'hiding', refusing to accept responsibility, because it implies hiding from ourselves, refusing to accept and acknowledge ourselves as we are.

In this account of Creation and the Fall, we are offered an insight into the human situation, the make-up of the human character. The apostle Paul sums up very powerfully the feeling that all of us have had at some point or other in our lives: the good things I want to do, I don't manage to do them; and I end up doing things I don't really want to! [See the quotation from Romans 7 in the box to the right.]

The Genesis account is about freedom, the freedom accorded in love by God – but it is also about the fear, the loneliness, the isolation and division that haunt the human condition. All of us are Adam and partner:

– we are not at peace with each other

– we are not at peace with God

– we are not at peace within ourselves.

This is what is meant by the theological expression 'original sin'. An unfortunate expression, in some ways, because the original state – in biblical terms – was innocence.

The consequence in the Genesis account is the expulsion from the Garden – but that is not where the story ends. God does not withdraw his breath from the creatures he has made, his life remains within us. Even though we chose to go contrary to God's way, he remains faithful to his love for his creation, and promises a redeemer.

Expelled from the Garden, yes. Abandoned by God, no. Adam and Eve (it is now she receives her name from Adam) and all who will be their children begin the long road to healing and reconciliation.

'COME BACK TO ME!'

The unfolding story of the children of Adam and Eve traced thoughout the Old Testament is that of the ongoing relationship between God and humankind – a relationship that continues to have its ups and its downs!

The first covenant established by creation has been breached – not completely shattered, for humankind still exists and is still 'in the image and likeness of God'. In the God-given freedom that this implies, the human person is free to acknowledge and renew this covenant – or to refuse it.

In the early chapters of Genesis, we also have the account of the destruction of the wicked but the saving of the just; Noah and the ark – with the rainbow poetically fixed in the heavens as the sign of the new, happier link between God and humankind once sin and evil have been destroyed.

When the Bible moves to historical figures, there is immediately the defining moment of the Covenant with Abraham, the alliance by which he becomes father of the chosen people of God.

When that people are in slavery in Egypt, God is seen to be keeping his covenant promise when he intervenes to rescue them: the passover of the angel of death and the crossing of the Red Sea into freedom, towards the Promised Land.

The time in the desert is legendary for its stories of grumbling and discontent by the people, usually resolved by signs of God's continuing love for them: when they are starving he sends them manna; when they are thirsty, water from the rock.

However, the great sign of his love is the giving of the Law of the Covenant, the tablets of stone on which the Ten Commandments are written. It is very important to note how the Ten Commandments begin: it is not by listing the famous Ten 'You shall . . .you shall not'. No, the Ten Commandments open with God restating *his* part in the Covenant.

I am the Lord your God
who brought you out of the land of
    Egypt
out of the house of slavery.
(Exodus 20:1-2; Deuteronomy 5:6)

The implications are clear: God is saying that if you want to stay truly free and avoid falling back into slavery, then here is how to do that . . . and only then are the commandments listed.

Does this great and seemingly definitive restatement of the Covenant fare any bet-

ter? Within hours the stone tablets are quite literally broken, for Moses descends to find that the people have 'forgotten' the Lord, and have made the golden calf. There is the terrible moment when, in a purge of the sinful people, 3,000 die. Then Moses prays to the Lord:

I am grieved,
this people have committed a grave sin
making themselves a god of gold.
And yet if it pleases you
to blot out this sin of theirs . . .
(Exodus 32:31)

So God promises to renew the Covenant; Moses prepares new tablets of stone and prays:

Forgive us our faults and our sins,
and adopt us as your heritage.
(Exodus 34:9)

Forty days and forty nights Moses stays with the Lord, writing the words of the Covenant on the tablets of stone. The tablets are enshrined in the gold-covered box known as the Ark of the Covenant, which is placed at the very heart, the holiest place in the Tabernacle – a movable sanctuary that would accompany the people on their pilgrimage through the desert to the Promised Land.

When the people are established in the Promised Land, have David as king and Jerusalem as capital, that movable sanctuary is replaced by the Temple – visible sign of the Covenant, of God's abiding presence with his people. It is not quite Eden restored, but here, in the Temple, God is present.

The Temple will function not just as the symbol of God's presence, but also as a sign of the people's unfaithfulness. Already, the Temple was constructed on a system of concentric areas, with the holiest in the centre: the Ark of the Covenant in the Holy of Holies. To come and to progress through the Temple was already a great process of purification. The symbolism of the Temple operate in another way, too: the prophets will interpret the loss of the Temple, particularly the great Exile, as punishment for their having abandoned their part in the contract, their alliance, their covenant with God.

The prophets use a host of images to portray a loving, faithful God and his fickle, often unfaithful people. The image of the vine, for example, on which God lavishes such loving care – but which proves fruitless (Hosea 10:1; Isaiah 27:1-2, 45:1-7; Jeremiah 2:21, 5:10, 6:9, 12:10; Ezekiel 15:1-8, 17:3-10, 19:10-14).

Another very evocative image used by the prophets is that of husband and wife: the husband who waits lovingly and patiently for the unfaithful wife to return (this image is explored more fully in the chapter on marriage: see pages 104-105).

There is a remarkable consistency in this unfolding history of the people's relationship with God. On the one hand there is the love of God, ever reaching out to offer his people true freedom. On the other, there is the hesitant progress of that people, happy to receive the blessings God showers on them, but not so good at maintaining their side of the alliance. It is all too easy, it seems, to be distracted by other apparent 'freedoms' and 'blessings'. This is exactly why we are offered Genesis 3 in the Bible. It is not about individuals called Adam and Eve: it is about every one of us. So the terrible question: is there no way that humankind can be definitively reconciled with God?

CHRIST CALLS US TO CONVERSION

When Christ begins his mission, his message is unambiguously clear.

The kingdom of God is at hand:
repent and believe in the Gospel.
(Mark 1:15)

Conversion means essentially turning towards God – and thereafter it implies turning away from anything that impedes progress towards God. Conversion is a life-long process, it is a journey. It means following Christ on his road to God.

Clearly, then, the first and greatest sacrament of conversion and reconciliation is that of baptism. Hence the great significance if the baptismal promises:

- three great promises of rejecting sin and evil

- three great promises of trust in and entrustment to God.

Baptism is our sharing in the great redeeming act of Christ's paschal mystery: his death, which destroys death and sin, because he rises again and promises us the new life of the resurrection. Here is the answer to that awful question: can there be no definitive healing in the broken covenant between God and humankind? Christ is the definitive answer, who, by his redeeming sacrifice, once and for all ransomed us with his blood and paid for us the price of Adam's sin. This is what the Church proclaims in song at the Easter Vigil:

> *This is the night*
> *when Christians everywhere*
> *are freed from all defilement,*
> *are restored to grace*
> *and walk together in holiness . . .*
> *The power of this holy night*
> *dispels all evil, washes guilt away,*
> *restores lost innocence . . .*
> *Night truly blest,*
> *when heaven is wedded to earth*
> *and man is reconciled to God!*

(from the *Exsultet* of the Easter Vigil Liturgy)

So, Paul writes to the Christians at Corinth:

> *You were washed*
> *you were sanctified*
> *you were justified*
> *in the name of the Lord Jesus*
> *and in the Spirit of our God.*
> (1 Corinthians 6:11)

But Christ, no more than God, does not oblige anyone to follow him. Nor does he, nor can he, constrain those who set out on the journey of following him never to turn back. Created in God's image and likeness, conformed to the image of Christ in Christian initiation – but ever free. So, the Church is indeed 'holy', but is made up of people who are sinners.

In this sense, the Church is in need of constant purification, and the life of the Church is one of constant renewal: at every step of the way, the Church, and members of the Church must decide if this step is taking them nearer to God; or whether it represents a pause on that route, or worse, a turning back, away from God.

Redeemed, yes. But sin is still with us. John writes bluntly in his First Letter:

If we say we have no sin,
we deceive ourselves!
(1 John 1:8)

'I WILL GO TO MY FATHER . . .'

And if we discover that we have stopped moving towards God, or even turned away from him? Jesus offers us the magnificent parable of the two sons. (Luke 15:11-24): 'A man had two sons . . .'. The younger asks for his share in the inheritance, he leaves, and for a long time revels in the pleasure that seems to be the fruit of that inheritance. What freedom! To do what he likes! Until the money runs out. Extreme misery follows, which reaches its worst point in the humiliation of looking after pigs, and being jealous of their food!

The turning point: he reflects on what he has lost, and perceives that he may even have lost his genuine inheritance: 'I no longer deserve to be called my father's son.' And yet in saying this, he is acknowledging where his true inheritance lies. He resolves to return, to admit his guilt before his father and to ask to be accepted back – not as son, just as servant. He sets out on the journey back to the father.

While he was still a long way off, the father saw him and was moved with pity. He ran to the boy, clasped him in his arms and kissed him tenderly (Luke 15:20).

The son tries to admit his mistake, but already the father has welcomed him back as son, and his joy bursts into feasting and celebration:

We are going to have a feast,
a celebration,
because this son of mine was dead
and has come back to life:
he was lost and is found.
(Luke 15:24)

The story, as told by Jesus, does not end here, but continues with the attitude of the other son. We shall return to this later.

The parable Jesus recounts presents a magnificent picture of the forgiving father. But Jesus went further than recounting stories: the forgiving love of God the Father was shown in practice by Christ in his lifetime. Jesus explicitly invokes 'the authority of the Son of Man to forgive sins' and he not only heals but forgives the paralytic (Mark 2:1-12, especially verses 5 and 10).

One thing is very clear: during his public life Jesus not only forgave sins, but also made plain the effect of this forgiveness: he reintegrated forgiven sinners into the community of the People of God from which sin had alienated or even excluded them. (cf. **Catechism** 1443)

This is the message that Jesus taught in the parable from Luke 15, when he refers to the other son. He, it would seem, had remained faithful to the father, but he now resents the love lavished on the younger, faithless son. The father has to correct him, and repeats:

Your brother here was dead
and has come back to life;
he was lost and is found.
(Luke 15:32)

Here is a fundamental truth about conversion and reconciliation: it means not only turning away from sin and turning back to God; it also means welcoming back all those who turn back to the Father.

FORGIVENESS ENTRUSTED TO THE CHURCH

After his resurrection, Christ entrusts to the apostles this same God-given mission of forgiving sin and reconciling sinners back to the family of God, the Church.

In John's Gospel the forgiveness of sins is quite clearly the first fruits of the resurrection – fruits that the apostles must continue to make present in the world as necessary: On the evening of Easter day Jesus came and stood among them. He said to them 'Peace be with you' and showed them his hands and his side. The disciples were filled with joy when they saw the Lord, and he said to them again,

'Peace be with you.
As the Father sent me,
so I am sending you.'
And saying this he breathed on them
and said:
'Receive the Holy Spirit.
For those whose sins you forgive,
they are forgiven;
for those whose sins you retain,
they are retained.'
(John 20:20-23)

The ecclesial dimension, the fact that reconciliation is also about being welcomed back by and into the Church, is expressed more clearly in Matthew's Gospel. Jesus tells his disciples: 'If your brother does something wrong, go and have it out with him alone, between your two selves. If he listens to you, you have won back your brother. If he does not listen, take one or two others along with you . . . But if he refuses to listen to these, report it to the community, and if he refuses to listen to the community, treat him like a pagan or an outcast:

I tell you solemnly,
whatever you bind on earth

shall be considered bound in heaven;
whatever you loose on earth
shall be considered loosed in heaven.
(Matthew 18:15-18)

Already, earlier in Matthew's Gospel, when Peter makes his great profession of faith and publicly says in the name of the disciples, 'You are the Christ, the Son of the living God,' Jesus' response is to 'build the Church' on such a clear declaration of faith. As part of this church-building, Jesus promises:

I will give you the keys of the kingdom:
whatever you bind on earth
shall be considered bound in heaven;
whatever you loose on earth
shall be considered loosed in heaven.
(Matthew 16:19-20)

The 'binding' and 'loosing' already had a clear meaning in the Jewish tradition: it signified precisely judging, on the basis of their behaviour, who was and who was not a member of the community. Someone who was obviously tied up with sin was excluded, excommunicated; when that person proved by their changed life-style that they were free of sin, they could be 'loosed' from excommunication and reconciled with the community.

So Christ entrusted to the apostles the authority in Christ's name and with the power of the Spirit, to assure sinners of the forgiveness of God's pardon; and to reconcile sinners back into the family of the Church. How did the apostles and their successors put this mission into practice?

> *It was God*
> *who reconciled us*
> *to himself*
> *through Christ,*
> *and Christ gave us*
> *the work of handing on*
> *this reconciliation.*
> (2 Corinthians 5:18)

HISTORY

The way in which penance has been celebrated in the Church has varied considerably over the years, probably more than in any other sacrament.

The Early Church

If we explore the texts of the New Testament we find there are two distinct attitudes to sin and its forgiveness, which seem to correspond to the seriousness of the fault.

The sacrament of conversion in the New Testament is baptism: thereafter, turning toward God and turning one's back on sin are considered as the standard way of living out the Christian life. The practical ways in which this sense of penance operated was through prayer, fasting, almsgiving and other good works (see Matthew 6:1-18). Through these, the imperfections in the Christian's life were rectified; these were the instruments of whatever forgiveness was needed.

However, it is also very clear in the New Testament that there are certain actions which are so blatantly out of step with the baptismal commitment that the person has effectively placed themselves outside the communion that baptism implies. This is the original sense of 'excommunication'. It is not so much that the Church excommunicates someone, expels them from the Church; rather, the individual is behaving like someone who has never been baptised, and, where necessary for the good of the other baptised, the Church publicly states that this individual is 'excommunicated'. A direct consequence is exclusion from eucharistic communion, but it was first and foremost exclusion from the Christian communion, the fellowship of the faithful.

In his First Letter to the community at Corinth (1 Cor 5), Paul explains to them that expelling a certain individual from the community is something they should have done, because:

> *I have been told that someone is living with his father's wife. This is a case of sexual immorality that must be unparalleled even among pagans . . . a man who does a thing like that ought to have been expelled from the community.*
> (1 Corinthians 5:1-2)

Notice Paul's argument: this person's behaviour shows what he is really like, worse than a pagan. He is declaring publicly by his behaviour that he is not a Christian, therefore . . .

> *. . . with the power of the Lord Jesus he is to be handed over to Satan . . .*
> (1 Corinthians 5:5)

which sounds like a definitive judgement, but in fact the purpose is to convert the person concerned, to turn him round,

> *. . . so that his sensual body may be destroyed and his spirit saved on the day of the Lord.*
> (1 Corinthians 5:5)

This fundamental intuition that sin is reneging on the promises in baptism was to be expressed in the way the early Church celebrated the power of forgiveness entrusted to her by Christ.

First of all, the sins that were concerned by the sacrament were those which demonstrated clearly to everyone that the individual had abandoned their baptismal promises: the sins, then, needed to be public, and grave: examples were apostasy (denying the faith and anything which implied it such as indulging publicly in pagan rituals), murder and adultery.

Secondly, what was required was a reconversion, which was modelled on the first sacrament of conversion, namely baptism. Hence, just as there was a rite which marked the entry of those seeking conversion into the ranks of the catechumens, so there was a rite of entry into the ranks of those seeking reconversion, whose technical name was 'penitents'. The ashes we use on Ash Wednesday are a trace of one of the rites that accompanied this entry into the rite of penitents, which was a public admission by the person of their need to learn again to be a Christian. Like the catechumens, the penitents had a special place within the assembly; they could stay for the Sunday Liturgy of the Word, but they could not stay for the Eucharist. The penitents had to pass through a period of retraining, parallel to the catechumens: reading scripture, praying, and involvement in the charitable work of the church. This lasted long enough for them to prove themselves. It was always a matter of several years.

Just as for the catechumens, when it was judged that the penitents were ready to be received back into the Christian community, they were convoked to the Mass for the reconciliation of penitents. Just as for Christian initiation, this reintegration into Christ and into the community was presided over by the bishop. In the Roman rite, this Mass was celebrated on Holy Thursday morning, so that the reconciled penitents would be able to take part in the Church's greatest feast, the Paschal Vigil.

It is easy to see why the oldest reference we have to the sacrament outside of the New Testament speaks of 'second baptism' and makes the distinction between the two by saying penance is the 'baptism of tears' (Pastor of Hermas). Saint Ambrose speaks of there being two conversions in the Church . . . there are water and tears, the water of baptism and the tears of repentance (Ambrose, Letter 41:12). Tertullian makes a parallel using a different metaphor: after having being saved by baptism, penance is the second plank after the shipwreck which is the loss of grace (Tertullian, *On Penance* 4,2).

Just as baptism could only be received once, so – the Church ruled – penance could only be received once. Committing another grave public sin meant definitive expulsion from the community. This led to people postponing presenting themselves for penance as late as possible in life, and it became widespread to wait until people were dying.

The order of the elements that constituted the overall process was:
– public entry into the order of penitents because of a publicly known and grave sin
– completion of a very long period of penance
– absolution (granted by the bishop).

And this sacrament could only be received once.

The Celtic influence (Sixth century onwards)

The Celtic Church, with its roots in a society where there had already existed a sacred brotherhood (the Druids), was built on a pattern of communities centred around monasteries rather than parishes, but monasteries in which it was traditional for all or most of the monks to be ordained priests. Another cultural feature of the Celts was a system or at least a sense of law that was based on atonement.

Already in the monastic communities of the East, there had been a custom of monks acting as spiritual advisers to each other. Part of which would involve a brother seeking advice about his Christian life, discussing what was wrong in his life, and asking for prayer and guidance. These monks, however, were not ordained.

In the Celtic culture, the personal, individual consultation with the priestly brotherhood that may have happened with Druids was easily Christianised, and there was an abundance of ordained priests available to the people. So penance took on a so-called 'private' form. The sinner would come to the priest, seeking God's forgiveness which was expressed through absolution given by priest. The solemn entry into penance, presenting oneself to the community as a sinner in public was gone, but presenting oneself as a sinner to a representative of that community remained. The nature of the sins concerned evolved. In public penance, the sin was known already: what mattered was admitting the need for forgiveness. Now, in the 'private' form of the sacrament, 'private' sins need to be admitted, and so we have the development of a specific confessing of one's sins.

Again influenced by the culture in which this Church was implanted, the Celtic monks imposed a penance which was calculated on the gravity and nature of the sin. In order for the penance to be properly calculated, then, the priest needed to know exactly what sins had been committed and how many times. Penitential books were drawn up, which listed sins and their corresponding 'tariff' or penance. Originally, under this Celtic system, penance still had to be completed before the penitent could receive absolution. Penances had 'equivalences': so a two-day fast could be substituted by 100 psalms and 100 genuflections or by 1,500 genuflections: pastorally, the original idea was that the penance should correspond to the capacities of the penitent. But because of the cultural notion that one person could atone for another, the penitent could invite (and

PUBLIC AND PRIVATE PENANCE

Rabanus Maurus, Bishop of Mayence († 856), instructed his priests as follows:

If the fault is public, everyone knows about it and it has scandalised the entire Christian community, then the sinner must have hands laid on him at the entry to the choir. But if the faults are secret ones, and the sinner confesses them freely to the bishop or to the priest in private, then the fulfilment of penance too, shall remain private. In this way, the simple faithful in the Church will not be scandalised by seeing public expiations for which they do not know the reason.

(On instructing the clergy II, 30)

THROUGHOUT HISTORY . . .

Beneath the changes in discipline and celebration that this sacrament has undergone over the centuries, the same fundamental structure is to be discerned. It comprises two equally essential elements: on the one hand, the acts of the man or woman who undergoes conversion through the action of the Holy Spirit: namely, contrition, confession, and satisfaction; on the other, God's action through the intervention of the Church. The Church, who through the bishop and his priests forgives sins in the name of Jesus Christ and determines the manner of satisfaction, also prays for the sinner and does penance with him or her. Thus the sinner is healed and re-established in ecclesial communion.

(Catechism 1448)

eventually pay) another to help him with his penance. So, if the penance was the recitation of the complete psalter, one might pay three monks to recite 50 psalms each! This meant that even the severest of penances could be accomplished fairly quickly. This reached the point where the priest granting absolution could be certain that the penance would be rapidly completed, so all that was demanded before absolution was a promise that the penance would be fulfilled.

The key features of this practice were:

– confession is made privately, covering all sins; detailed confession is necessary so that the appropriate penance can be set

– confession is made to a priest

– who stipulates a penance but who grants absolution before this penance is completed

– the penance is completed.

This practice could be repeated.

The missionary Irish monks brought this tradition with them into Europe. Of course, at the beginning there was a prudent reluctance on the part of some other churches to adopt such a radically different practice: the Council of Toledo (589), for example, did not accept the Celtic practice, but the Council of Châlons (644-645) did. The positive value of the personal spiritual guidance in this practice plus the sacramental assurance of forgiveness for 'private' sins obviously corresponded to a pastoral need, because by the Middle Ages this practice was commonplace. However, it is important to understand that this 'private' form complemented the older public form. The two existed in parallel: a public celebration for public sins; a 'private' form' for 'private' sins (see the quote from Rabanus Maurus in the margin column left).

Pilgrimage, and in due course, taking part in a crusade were also fundamentally penitential. In some cases, making a pilgrimage or being sent on the crusades was the penance imposed sacramentally. For many, these were undertaken on a personal spiritual initiative, with the aim of achieving forgiveness for sins.

By the ninth century, the idea that penance *could* be repeated had evolved to the conviction that it *should* be repeated, at least once a year.

Middle Ages

The twelfth century is the period of the Scholastics, the great effort at making systematic sense of our relationship with God through the Church, and especially through the liturgy. Abelard wrote at length on the value of contrition. For Thomas Aquinas, the act of confession was important: he was building a sacramental theology based on 'matter' and 'form', which worked relatively easily for sacraments where the 'matter' was self-evident (water for baptism, bread and wine for the Eucharist). For the sacrament of penance, what was the physical sign, the 'matter'? Aquinas focused on the human act of confessing one's sins, because it is an external sign which is visible, and it is social (it requires at least one other person to hear it).

Gradually, the doublet of confession-absolution took central importance. In the thirteenth century, though the traditional form of public penance was still to be found in the liturgical books, it was in fact now practised as follows:

– the penitent knelt before the priest, in a sign of humility, and both made the sign of the cross.

– the penitent made confession. This was now considered the essential element, the painful effort and the humility required to make confession being seen as 'penance', suffering that brought forgiveness of sins.

– the priest urged the penitent to conversion and contrition, with only the briefest reference to the word of God

– absolution was granted in the declarative formula *Ego te absolvo,* 'I forgive you…' This was fixed as the 'sacramental form' by the Council of Florence (1439); until now it had been in the deprecative form, that is 'May God forgive . . .'

– 'satisfaction' (see the technical definition of this on page 77) was performed by the penitent, seen as a complement to the mortification of 'confessing'.

Corresponding to this usage, with the

centrality and importance of the act of confessing sins, the sacrament was now described as 'Confession'. Recourse to the sacrament became more frequent. The Fourth Lateran Council (1215), stipulated that all sinners must confess their sins at least once a year.

The Council of Trent, looking principally to the theology of the Scholastics, presented the order of acts by the penitent in the sacrament as: contrition-confession-absolution-satisfaction. Moreover, contrition was given a very particular meaning: it could only be 'perfect' within the sacrament, that the only genuine contrition was one which implied making confession and receiving absolution.

Intended to express the theological value of the sacrament in the forgiveness of sins, this had the effect, in practice, of making the sacrament seem the only way to receive forgiveness of sins. The other means of exercising penance in the Christian life were supplanted, to the extent that penance became 'devotional': spiritual direction and the need for penance in life became identified with sacramental 'Confession', as it is now being called.

In the Ritual (1614), revised on the Council of Trent's instructions, some effort is made to restore a sense of celebration to the sacrament. The appropriate vestments are stipulated (a stole), and the priest and penitent should be separated by a grill. This meant that the priest's gesture of laying his hand on the penitent was now reduced to a symbolic raising of the right hand in the direction of the penitent.

The sacrament, then, had lost its ecclesial and its social character. It was considered as 'private'. Its title, 'Confession', referred only to one part, instead of to the overall process of turning away from sin and turning back to God. 'Confession', in referring to the act of the penitent, seemed to make the sinner the 'active' person in the sacrament instead of the saving act of Christ. The individual penitent might make reference to scripture in his personal preparation, but scripture had disappeared from the celebration of the rite itself. However, it was conducted mainly in the vernacular, reverting to Latin for the absolution.

PENANCE TODAY

Vatican II, in its Decree on the Liturgy demanded that …

the rite and formulas for the sacrament of penance are to be revised so that they express more clearly both the nature and the effect of the sacrament.

(Sacrosanctum Concilium 72)

Already, the Council has reverted to the title of 'penance' rather than 'confession'.

This rather simply expressed demand, which does not explain what the nature and effect of penance are, can be better understood when we note the Council's explanation of penance in *Lumen Gentium*, Vatican II's great document on the Church. In the chapter on the laity, the people of God, the Council says:

Those who approach the sacrament of penance obtain pardon from the mercy of God for offences committed against him. They are at the same time reconciled with the Church, which they have wounded by their sins, and which by charity, example and prayer seeks their conversion.

(Lumen Gentium 11)

Earlier in the same document, reflecting on the nature of the Church, the Council says:

Christ was sent by the Father 'to bring good news to the poor, to heal the contrite of heart' (Lk 4:18), 'to seek and to save what was lost' (Lk 19:10). Similarly the Church encompasses with love all those who are afflicted with human weakness.…

While Christ 'holy, innocent, undefiled' (Heb 7:26), knew nothing of sin (2 Cor 5:21), but came to expiate only the sins of the people (cf. Heb 2:17), the Church, embracing sinners in her bosom, is at the same time holy and always in need of being purified, and incessantly pursues the path of penance and renewal.

(Lumen Gentium, 8)

Here is a magnificent statement of the nature and effect of penance! The task was to concretise this ideal in a revised rite.

When the Rite was promulgated in 1974 (exactly ten years to the day after the promulgation of the document on the liturgy), it had as its title *Ordo Pænitentiæ*, translated in English as the *Rite of Penance*. It deliberately avoids saying 'the sacrament of penance', thereby returning to the New Testament vision of the whole Christian life as being a work of conversion, turning away from sin and toward God. The Rite quotes *Lumen Gentium 8*, and insists that this continual repentance is accomplished and perfected by the people of God in many different ways.

How? By sharing in the sufferings of Christ through enduring their own difficulties, by carrying out works of mercy and charity, by adopting ever more fully the outlook of the Gospel message (cf. Rite of Penance 4). In this way it is the people of God who become the 'sacrament' of conversion to God.

All of this is expressed in various ways in the life of the Church. The Rite continues: it happens each and every time the faithful confess they are sinners and ask pardon of God and of their brothers and sisters.

Only then does the Rite move on to mention the sacrament of penance, which again is presented in the words of *Lumen Gentium* 11:

In the sacrament of penance:

— *the faithful obtain from the mercy of God pardon for their sins against him*
— *they are reconciled with the Church which they have wounded by their sins*
— *the Church works for their conversion by charity, example and prayer.*

Of course, the bulk of the Rite of Penance is taken up by offering the way in which the sacrament of penance is celebrated, and that is what we shall now explore. But it is important to see how, for the Rite, the sacrament – which itself is proposed in several different forms – is only part of the lifelong process of turning away from sin and turning to God to which all the baptised are called.

OUTLINE

For the celebration of the sacrament, the Church now offers, in broad terms, two forms: one individual, the other as a community celebration. Within the community celebration, there are parts which can – and normally are – administered individually. On the following page is an outline presentation, showing the parallels between the different forms the celebration of the sacrament can take.

The parallels are not always exact, but from this overview the general structure of the celebration of the sacrament should be clear. Whether celebrated in the individual form, or in the communal form:

* there is a moment of welcome
* time is taken to let God's word be heard in the form of a reading from scripture
* the sacrament includes confession, accepting a sign of conversion and penance, and absolution
* a moment of thanksgiving for the mercy received from God.

Let us explore the various elements that fit into this fundamentalstructure, and which articulate the dialogue between sinner and God which becomes a celebration of God's loving forgiveness.

PREPARATION

Penance is a lifelong process. Even when we focus on a particular celebration of the sacrament of penance, there is a very real sense in which it does not begin with the opening hymn. It begins from the moment we decide to take part in the celebration of the sacrament, because thereby we are already acknowledging that we are in need of the forgiveness that the sacrament offers.

THE WORD OF GOD

In the communal rite, there is more time given to a shared preparation, which is guided by sharing several texts from scripture, by the homily, and by a shared examination of conscience.

In the individual rite, these elements should still be present, but in a concise and

RITE FOR THE RECONCILIATION OF INDIVIDUAL PENITENTS	RITE FOR THE RECONCILIATION OF SEVERAL PENITENTS	
INTRODUCTORY RITES (Reception of the Penitent) Greeting and Sign of the cross	**INTRODUCTORY RITES** Sign of the cross and Greeting Admonition Opening prayer	
Invitation to trust Revelation of state of life **LITURGY OF THE WORD** Reading	**LITURGY OF THE WORD** First reading Responsorial psalm Gospel acclamation Gospel reading Homily Examination of conscience	
(Brief discussion of reading)	**WITH INDIVIDUAL CONFESSION AND INDIVIDUAL ABSOLUTION**	**WITH GENERAL CONFESSION AND GENERAL ABSOLUTION**
LITURGY OF RECONCILIATION	**LITURGY OF RECONCILIATION** General confession of sins Lord's Prayer Prayer by the priest	**LITURGY OF RECONCILIATION** Sign of repentance
Confession of sins and Acceptance of satisfaction Penitent's prayer of sorrow Lord's Prayer or psalm (prayed with priest)	Individual confession of sins and Acceptance of satisfaction	General confession of sins
Absolution	Individual absolution Exhortation	General absolution
Proclamation of God's praise	Proclamation of praise Concluding prayer of thanksgiving	Proclamation of praise
CONCLUDING RITES	**CONCLUDING RITES** Blessing	
Dismissal	Dismissal	

condensed form. The reading from scripture may be simply a sentence or two, a compelling phrase taken from one of the Gospels, for example. A good confessor will take a little time to suggest how even these few words should enlighten all that follows. The rite indicates that in the individual rite the scripture extract may be proposed either by the penitent or the confessor. (See the list of texts proposed for reconciliation of individual penitents in the margin column to the left.)

An ideal way to prepare as a penitent for the individual form of celebration is to choose the passage of scripture around which everything else will be built and take its sense. This should normally be a passage from scripture which speaks of God's great love for us. It could be a poetic expression of this from one of the psalms, or a narrative which illustrates it in a more concrete way, or a Gospel passage where Jesus heals or teaches. We might then imagine ourselves into that scripture text: how do the sentiments expressed there compare with mine? How do the characters in the passage respond to the love of God? And how do I respond?

In practice, I could write the passage out – which would not only help me to assimilate its message, but would give me a copy which I could offer to the priest, and tell him that this is the text I used for my preparation.

THE EXAMINATION OF CONSCIENCE

This expression 'examination of conscience' is a traditional one – but one which is often used without paying attention to what it means and implies. Literally, it means that I set out to explore who I am: that, in particular, I look honestly at the way I behave, and from those signs work back to what motivates my life – not just in individual actions, but as a whole.

Self-exploration is always a worthwhile, but a tricky enterprise. Left entirely to ourselves, we almost inevitably cheat, give ourselves the benefit of the doubt, make excuses for ourselves! This is the great value of the time offered with the sacrament for a shared examination of conscience. However, we still need to make time for the essential discipline of self-examination of conscience.

One traditional way is to take the Ten Commandments, and use them as a measure of our behaviour. This is very valid, as long as we remember how the Ten Commandments start: 'I am the Lord your God, who brought you out of slavery . . . (Exodus 20:1-2; Deuteronomy 5:6 – see page 64). The real question in an examination of conscience is, how – despite the promise of freedom from God – have I let myself become enslaved in one way or another by other things? What kind of things enslave me, and to what degree? What things distract me from God? from my loyalty to God? What things get in the

way of my relationship with others? What more might I be doing to build that relationship with God and with others?

My faults and my sins operate as negative sacraments, or as sacraments in reverse: my actions are the visible signs of my deep-rooted attitudes. A doctor needs to treat not only the pain, the symptoms, but he needs to discover the illness that is provoking those pains. So too the sacrament offers us healing in our spiritual life – but what we need to present for healing are not the symptoms, the individual actions, but the underlying attitudes that provoke them. This is what needs 'conversion', what has to be 'turned around'.

OPENING RITES
Welcome

For the celebration with individual penitents, the Rite says specifically in the introduction that the priest should welcome the penitent with fraternal charity and expects that this be expressed in friendly words (Rite of Penance 16).

When the Rite presents this moment of the celebration, it says:

the priest welcomes the penitent warmly and greets him or her with kindness.
(Rite of Penance 41)

The Rite, however, does not put words into the priest's mouth: these must come from the heart if they are to be 'warm' and 'kind'.

Just as we have said that the sacrament begins from the moment the penitent decides that he or she has need of it, so too the welcome the penitent will receive needs to be ever-evident, so as to draw the penitent to seek the sacrament. Here is an important moment of the celebration that needs constant attention. In as much as the priest represents the community, we ought to explore the ways in which the community can make this welcome more palpable. Are the places where the sacrament is offered 'warm' and inviting? Are the times and availability of the sacrament presented in a 'kindly' way, that will encourage people to take part?

These same questions are valid for the communal celebration too. Already, the fact that the celebration is communal should mark the atmosphere. This needs to be reinforced, however; for example, does the opening hymn encourage a sense of being welcomed 'warmly and with kindness'?

The sign of the cross

Making the sign of the cross can become very routine, yet it has a real significance in this sacrament. It places all that is about to happen under God's protection and guidance – as it does when used at the beginning of any prayer or celebration. More importantly, by the sign and by the invocation of the Trinity, it is a reminder of our first great sacrament of forgiveness, our baptism. In coming to the sacrament of penance and reconciliation we are renewing our baptism; God will pardon our sins: as in baptism we are united – in this case reunited – with the Church.

LITURGY OF THE WORD
Readings

The sacrament of penance is turning back to God. But how are we to turn back unless we hear him call us? This is why the Liturgy of the Word is an essential element of this sacrament – even in the form with individual penitents. It is in scripture that God reveals his love for us, that we hear him calling us back to him.

Through the Word of God the Christian receives light to recognise his or her sins and is called to conversion and confidence in God's mercy.
(Rite of Penance 17)

The faithful listen together to the Word of God, which proclaims his mercy and invites them to conversion; at the same time they examine the conformity of their lives with that Word of God (cf. Rite of Penance 22).

The sacrament of penance should always begin with a hearing of God's Word, because, through his Word, God calls men and women to repentance and leads them to true conversion of heart...

Readings should be chosen which illustrate the following:

a. the voice of God calling men and women back to conversion and even greater conformity with Christ

b. the mystery of our reconciliation through the death and resurrection of Christ and through the gift of the Holy Spirit

c. the judgement of God about good and evil in human lives as a help in the examination of conscience
(Rite of Penance 24)

Homily

As always, the homily should take its cue from the reading and, particularly during this celebration, should lead the penitents to examine their consciences, and to turn away from sin and toward God.

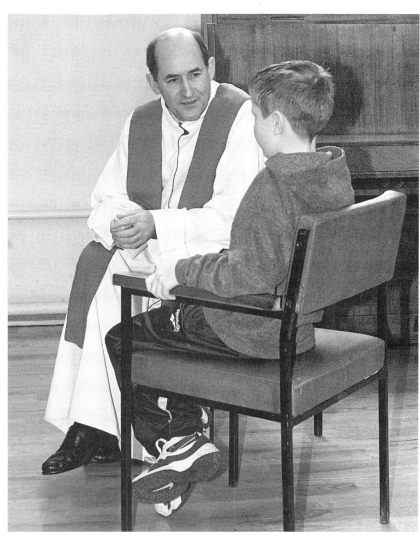

It should remind the faithful that sin works against God, against the community and against one's neighbours, and against the sinner (Rite of Penance 25).

Examination of conscience

If a conventional homily has been given, the Rite proposes a suitable period of silence for examining one's conscience and awakening true contrition for sin (Rite of Penance 26).

This need not be in complete silence: the celebrant, or the one who gave the homily might echo parts of it, or of the readings, as prompts to the examination of conscience.

The Rite suggests that, where it is judged pastorally appropriate, the homily can be constructed as a communal examination of conscience and awakening of contrition; of course, since this will be functioning as the homily, 'it should be clearly based on the text of scripture that has just been read' (Rite of Penance 26).

Where it is a celebration of several penitents with general confession and absolution, the homily needs to make sure that those who take part understand the implications:

- that each one should be sorry for his or her sins
- that each one must resolve to avoid committing them again. In particular, this means that anyone who has caused scandal and harm must have the firm intention of repairing this.

Confession

This sacrament came to be called 'confession' because of the central importance that the disclosure of personal sins came to have. But this is only part of the real meaning of 'confession'.

It is important to remember that the sacrament of penance is a celebration. So what are we celebrating? Our sins? No, rather we are celebrating the *forgiveness* of our sins. It is first and foremost a confession – that is, acknowledgement and praise – of the holiness of God and of his mercy towards sinful humanity (cf. Catechism 1424).

> *Whoever confesses his sins . . .*
> *is already working with God.*
> *God indicts your sins;*
> *if you also indict them,*
> *you are joined with God.*
> *Man and sinner are, so to speak,*
> *two realities:*
> *when you hear 'man' –*
> *this is what God has made;*
> *when you hear 'sinner' –*
> *this is what man himself has made.*
> *Destroy what you have made,*
> *so that God may save*
> *what he has made.*
> *. . . When you begin to abhor*
> *what you have made,*
> *it is then that*
> *your good works are beginning,*
> *since you are accusing yourself*
> *of your evil works.*
> *The beginning of good works*
> *is the confession of evil works.*
> *You do the truth*
> *and come to the light.*
>
> *[Saint Augustine,*
> *Commentary on John's Gospel 12,13]*
> *(quoted in Catechism 1458)*

Secondly, by the fact that we accept to make this disclosure to a minister of the Church, we are confessing, re-proclaiming so as to renew our baptism. We are making a public statement, confirming our belonging to the Church, our need of the Church.

Of course, within both of these, there is the necessary admission that we have need of God's mercy and forgiveness, and that we need to restore the link with the Church that we have damaged in some way. But in both cases, the admission of faults is not an end in itself, but part of a greater 'confession' of faith in God and of praise for his plan of salvation, a plan in which I confess I am personally caught up.

There is another sense in which the sacrament is a 'confession': by celebrating this sacrament I am professing my profound belief in God, in his love for me. I confess that he is my loving Father, which is why I confidently can then say, like the prodigal son in the parable 'I have sinned against you . . .'

It is because confession implies all these that the Church insists that

confession to a priest is an essential part of the sacrament of Penance.
(Catechism 1457)

Viewed in this larger and more positive sense, the real question is not 'What do I have to confess?' (meaning as little as possible!), but rather, 'What will help make proclaim God's merciful forgiveness toward me?' It is difficult to see how such a positive declaration can be genuine if I deliberately hold back on major flaws in my life and behaviour, which is why the Church stipulates that 'all mortal sins' should be confessed (see margin column on page 74). The Catechism (1457) recommends that even everyday faults (venial sins) be confessed, as part of opening ourselves up to the healing that Christ offers us.

Satisfaction

Here 'satisfaction' is the technical name given to what is more popularly known as the 'penance': in other words, the gesture by which we demonstrate our turning away from sin and turning back to God. Normally this will be one of the elements that make up the lifelong process of moving towards God: praying, fasting, works of mercy, an act of self-denial.

These acts of penance allow us to recover our status as co-heirs with the risen Christ – sharing his glory, provided we suffer with him (cf. Romans 8:17). It is very important to understand that the 'satisfaction' we make for our sins only has sense and meaning in as much as they are done 'through Jesus Christ'.

The Act of Sorrow

In our historical exploration we saw that it was twelfth-century theological reflection that brought this element of 'contrition' to the fore. This is the theology we still find in today's Catechism, which simply offers a direct quote from the Council of Trent:

Contrition is 'sorrow of the soul and detestation for the sin committed, together with the resolution not to sin again'
(Catechism 1451)

The Rite of Penance also quotes the Council of Trent word for word – but it adds the following (which is a quotation from Pope Paul VI):

*We can only approach the Kingdom of Christ by **metanoia**. This is a profound change of the whole person by which one begins to consider, judge and arrange his or her life according to the love of God, made manifest in his Son and offered to us in abundance.*
(Hebrews 1:2; Col 1:19 and passim)

The Rite continues:

the genuineness of penance depends on this heartfelt contrition.
(see Rite of Penance 6a)

One way to appreciate the importance of 'contrition' is to see that just as the paschal mystery spans time, so does the celebration of that mystery in the sacrament of penance: past, present, future. Contrition is our identification with this:

– We have sinned: recognising that we are sinners, though, is not enough. We must be stirred by the call of God to be truly sorry for such sins.

– We are forgiven: we hear God's word of pardon.

– We resolve with God's help, not to sin in the future. In so doing we already anticipate the fulfilment of Christ's glory at the end of time, when there will be no more sin.

The Lord's Prayer

It is Jesus himself who taught us this prayer, in which we beg for God's forgiveness. If we pray as Jesus instructed, we consciously link the forgiveness that we offer to each other with the forgiveness that God will grant us (see Catechism 1425).

This gives the prayer Jesus gave us a heightened significance when used during the sacrament of penance. In the individual form of celebration, the Lord's Prayer is proposed as a shared prayer after absolution.

Canon 961

§1 General absolution, without prior individual confession, cannot be given to a number of penitents together, unless:

1 danger of death threatens and there is not time for the priest or priests to hear the confessions of the individual penitents;

2 there exists a grave necessity, that is, given the number of penitents, there are not enough confessors available properly to hear the individual confessions within an appropriate time, so that without fault of their own the penitents are deprived of the sacramental grace or of holy communion for a lengthy period of time. A sufficient necessity is not, however, considered to exist when confessors cannot be available merely because of a great gathering of penitents, such as can occur on some major feast day or pilgrimage.

§2 It is for the diocesan Bishop to judge whether the conditions required in §1, no. 2 are present; mindful of the criteria agreed with the other members of the Episcopal Conference, he can determine the cases of such necessity.

In the communal rite, saying this prayer, in public with others, should be especially symbolic, which is why the Rite says, somewhat bluntly:

> *The Lord's Prayer is never omitted.*
> (Rite of Penance 27)

In communal celebrations, the saying together of the Lord's Prayer is complemented by a prayer by the priest, such as:

> *Lord,*
> *draw near to your servants*
> *who in the presence of your Church*
> *confess that they are sinners.*
> *Through the ministry of the Church*
> *free them from all sin*
> *so that renewed in spirit*
> *they may give you thankful praise.*
> (Rite of Penance 205)

or

> *Father,*
> *our source of life,*
> *you know our weakness.*
> *May we reach out with joy*
> *   to grasp your hand*
> *and work more readily in your ways.*
> (Rite of Penance 54)

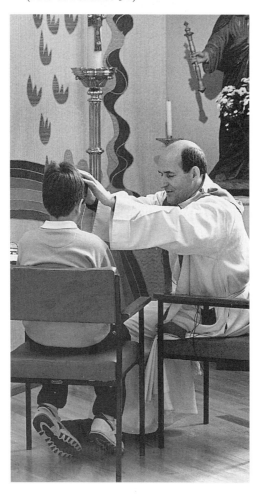

ABSOLUTION
Laying on of hands

In the celebration with an individual penitent the Rite stipulates that the priest should extend his hands over the penitent's head – adding in brackets, that at the very least he should extend his right hand toward the penitent (Rite of Penance 48).

As we have seen in other chapters (on confirmation, orders or anointing of the sick), the imposition of hands is an ancient sign which implies the transmission of power. Here, what is transmitted is the effect of that power, for it is God alone who can forgive sins: the Church, through the priest or bishop, operates as the sign and instrument of the forgiveness and reconciliation that Christ won for us at the price of his blood (see Catechism 1442).

Words of absolution

The new Rite keeps the formula that was first stipulated by the Council of Florence (see page 70) but has enlarged it with an eloquent introductory section which clearly expresses the essence of the sacrament:

– the Father of mercies is the source of all forgiveness

– it is through Christ's paschal mystery that our reconciliation is effected

– and through the power of his Spirit

– of which the Church is the minister:

> *God, the Father of mercies,*
> *through the death and resurrection*
> *   of his Son*
> *has reconciled the world to himself*
> *and sent the Holy Spirit among us for*
> *   the forgiveness of sins;*
> *through the ministry of the Church,*
> *may God give you pardon and peace,*
> *and I absolve you from your sins*
> *in the name of the Father*
> *and of the Son*
> *and of the Holy Spirit. Amen.*

When general absolution is given (and the conditions for when this may happen are strict, see the Code of Canon Law, left), this sacramental prayer of absolution can be preceded by a threefold blessing, which expresses the forgiveness that lies at the very heart of the being of God, Father, Son and Spirit.

God the Father does not wish the
  sinner to die
but to turn back to him and live.
He loved us first
  and sent his Son into the world to
  be its Saviour.
May he show you his merciful love
  and give you peace.
Amen.

Our Lord Jesus Christ was given up to
  death for our sins,
and rose again for our justification.
He sent the Holy Spirit on his apostles
and gave them power to forgive sins.
Through the ministry entrusted to me
may he deliver you from evil
and fill you with his Holy Spirit.
Amen.

The Spirit of the Comforter,
  was given to us
  for the forgiveness of sins.
In him we approach the Father.
May he cleanse your hearts
  and clothe you in his glory,
so that you may proclaim
  the mighty acts of God
who has called you out of darkness
  into the splendour of his light.
Amen.

Proclamation of God's praise

Here the traditional and positive meaning of 'confession' – acknowledging and praising God – has its explicit place. Such an outburst of praise is perhaps easier in the communal form, where we can all sing together (see Rite of Penance 29).

This moment of praise, however, is not absent from the individual form: after receiving pardon for his or her sins, the penitent praises the mercy of God and gives him thanks in a short invocation from scripture (see Rite of Penance 20). For example:

Priest: Give thanks to the Lord,
  for he is good.
Penitent: **For his love endures for
  ever!**

This theme of thanksgiving is continued in the communal celebration by the priest's prayer, which brings the Liturgy of Reconciliation to a close:

Father,
in your love you have brought us
  from evil to good
and from misery to happiness.
Through your blessings
give the courage of perseverance
to those you have called and justified
  by faith.
(Rite of Penance 62 [210])

Lord God,
creator and ruler of your kingdom of
  light,
in your great love for this world
you gave up your only Son
for our salvation.
His cross has redeemed us,
his death has given us life,
his resurrection has raised us to glory.
Through him we ask you
to be always present among your
  family.
Teach us to be reverent
  in the presence of your glory;
fill our hearts with faith,
our days with good works,
our lives with your love;
may your truth be on our lips
and your wisdom in all our actions,
that we may receive
  the reward of everlasting life.
(Rite of Penance [208])

ANOINTING OF THE SICK
Christ's healing touch

THE 'MYSTERY' OF SICKNESS AND OF SUFFERING

Nearly everyone who has suffered serious illness, or who has watched a loved one endure pain and discomfort has asked the question 'Why does this happen?' We are not the first generation to ask this question – nor shall we be the last. It is a question that haunts unbelievers and which believers too, must face. In some ways the question seems even more difficult for believers because, if God loves and cares for us, how can there be such pain and suffering?

Through the ages, great thinkers have tried to respond to this question of why God permits us to suffer, why God allows pain and illness to exist in the world.

They have come up with many theories and suggestions which can be summarised under three headings:

- **We bring it on ourselves**
  It is true that there are some illnesses that are the consequence of our life-style, because of ways in which we have abused out bodies, tried to push them too far. But it is far from being true about all suffering – especially that of children.

- **It is because we have sinned**
  It is true that some suffering is the result of sin. I can end up suffering because of my own sin, or because of the sins of others. But it is certainly not true of many victims of death and disease. Often, it is innocent people who suffer: children, again, for example. People who lead good lives are not exempt from suffering.

- **It is because God is angry and wants to punish us**
  This is really an extreme version of the explanation in the paragraph above. But as we have seen, it is not a satisfactory answer. Moreover, what kind of God would we have to believe in to say he wants to punish us? Is this the kind of God that Jesus revealed to us by his words and actions? Not at all!

We are left with our original question, then. And that is exactly what happens when the Bible explores the question of suffering. It dedicates a complete book to this question, the Book of Job. A good way to understand this Book is to imagine it as a play, or as a script for a film. Job is always centre stage, at the beginning as a good man on whom God has showered happiness and blessings of all kinds: family, wealth, health. As the drama unfolds, one by one these are taken from him. A whole succession of people pass, forcing him to try and answer the same question: why does God allow suffering? Job has to endure a whole series of disasters, each one worse than the previous, until he reaches the lowest possible point.

The answer of the Book of Job is that there is no answer! Job refuses to reply – because by the very fact of trying to answer why God allows suffering, you are admitting the impossible, you are obliged to say that what God wills for us is not good. The question is a trap, which Job refuses; Job's answer, if it can be called an answer, is to say:

The Lord has given,
the Lord has taken away.
Blessed be the will of the Lord.
(Job 1:21)

The Book of Job, written after the Law, the prophets and most of the psalms, tries to summarise the experience of the Jewish people, and how – given their relationship with God – they should deal with suffering.

Immediately after their escape from

Egypt, at their first moment of suffering in the desert (three days without water), through Moses they find fresh water, but above all, they receive this promise from God:

It is I, the Lord, who am your healer.
(Exodus 15:26)

However, this is only the conclusion of a promise, which begins,

If you listen carefully to the voice of the
*   Lord your God,*
and do what is right in his eyes,
if you pay attention to his
*   commandments*
and keep his statutes...

The Psalms show that people naturally and spontaneously turned to God in suffering: sometimes seeking consolation, like the whole of Psalm 38, which is a prayer in distress, and which concludes

Lord, do not desert me,
do not stand aside, my God!
Come quickly to my help,
Lord, my Saviour!
(Psalm 38:21-22)

Sometimes we can sense exasperation and even anger at suffering in the Psalms:

How much longer will you forget me,
*   Lord? For ever?*
How much longer will you hide your
*   face from me?*
How much longer must I endure grief
*   in my soul,*
and sorrow in my heart by day and by
*   night?*
Look and answer me, Lord my God!
(Psalm 13:1-3)

But ultimately, even in the face of overwhelming present suffering, the psalmist looks back to happier times, and forward in confidence, and so the song ends:

I for my part rely on your love, Lord;
let my heart sing your saving help.
Let me sing to the Lord
for the goodness he has shown me.
(Psalm 13: 5)

In the Psalms, the people of God turn to him as the Master of life and death. Above all, illness is often the starting point for a process of conversion, of turning back to God.

Largely because of the greatest suffering of the people, the time of their exile in Babylon, the Prophets came to understand and to teach the people that, paradoxically, suffering can heal; that suffering can be offered in atonement, for oneself and even for others. This is how Isaiah pictures the suffering Servant:

If he offers his life in atonement,
he shall see his heirs,
he shall have a long life
and through him
what the Lord wishes will be done.
His soul's anguish over
he shall see the light and be content.
By his sufferings
shall my servant justify many,
taking their faults on himself.
(Isaiah 53:10-11)

There is no human answer to the great question of suffering. The only answer the believer can give is to hold fast to the central belief that God loves us and cares for us, and that out of our pain and suffering God can and does draw good. The Bible's answer is that even the evil of pain and suffering can be turned, through the eyes of faith, into a great hymn of praise to God's glory: 'Blessed be the will of the Lord!'

Sometimes this praise is easier to proclaim than others. There are moments when we glimpse the power of God to turn the world upside down and defeat the destructive force of suffering. If we are lucky we may have experienced this great power of God in our own lives, or perhaps witnessed it in the lives of those close to us who were suffering. Not that the suffering necessarily disappears; but often the suffering person acquires an amazing dignity and nobility, which is not *despite* the pain, but which seems to grow out of and through it. Suffering, which at first seems to be a totally destructive force, is turned back to front, and is given a new meaning.

It is important, however, to notice that it is not in the suffering itself that we see reason to praise God. It is in the capacity of the human person to accept suffering, not in a simply passive way, but with determination and courage. It is taken on, confronted and thereby transformed. What could have destroyed in fact serves to build up; what could have been taken as a curse is converted into a blessing.

LIKE US IN ALL THINGS

In his *Letter to the Philippians* Paul quotes a hymn, a sung creed, which was used by the early Christians. (In fact, this is the oldest known Christian hymn.) It is a magnificent piece of poetic writing, six little phrases cleverly balanced into three about Christ humbling himself to become human and three about God glorifying Christ. What interests us here is the section concerning Christ:

> *His state was divine,*
> *yet he did not cling*
> *to his equality with God*
> *but emptied himself*
> *to assume the condition of a slave,*
> *and became as men are;*
> *and being as all men are*
> *he was humbler yet,*
> *even to accepting death,*
> *death on a cross.*
> (Philippians 2:6-8)

This ancient Christian song boldly declares the belief that is distinctly Christian, namely, that Jesus the Christ was fully human. God, in sending his son to be one like us, identified himself with every human experience. Like us he knew joy; like us, too, he knew pain and suffering.

We know from the Gospel accounts that Christ shared with us our fear and horror of suffering. In the Garden of Gethsemane, on the night before he died, Christ experienced the immense fearful anticipation of what lay ahead of him. He went so far as to ask to be delivered from that suffering: 'Father, take this cup away from me …' (Luke 22:42a). Jesus did not seek out suffering. However, when that suffering became inevitable, he accepted it: '… Nevertheless, let your will be done, not mine' (Luke 22:42b).

Christ's acceptance of suffering is not a passive one, however. In accepting suffering, Christ still maintains control, even throughout the worst indignities of his passion. Despite the efforts of his persecutors, his dignity and his nobility shine through. More importantly, we believe that through his willing acceptance of suffering and death, Christ transformed them utterly. Not only were Christ's sufferings turned to glory – as any brave person might manage – but in dying to rise again, Christ's sufferings become trophies of the greatest glory and the guarantee of what God really wants for all of us: life for ever with him.

As human beings, all our instincts want to reject suffering, because we know that suffering reflects the fact that something has gone wrong, that the balance which should exist in the world has been upset. The passion of Christ was a classic example of suffering caused by hatred and evil. This kind of suffering cannot be passively accepted. It must be fought and rejected. This is an unnecessary form of suffering, brought on by the wrong and sinful choices made by individuals or groups of people.

This is not true of all suffering, however. For a particular person, pain, suffering and illness may not be avoidable. The challenge that faces us as Christians is to associate ourselves with Christ and thereby transform that suffering into a source of glory, not least on a human level.

This is not easy, particularly when we are confronted with suffering and pain which is not caused by others: what are we to say of the handicapped person, the terminally ill cancer patient, the chronically sick, or the increasing weakness of the elderly. How are we to respond to all this? Can we find God in any of this? What should our attitude be to these mysteries of the human condition?

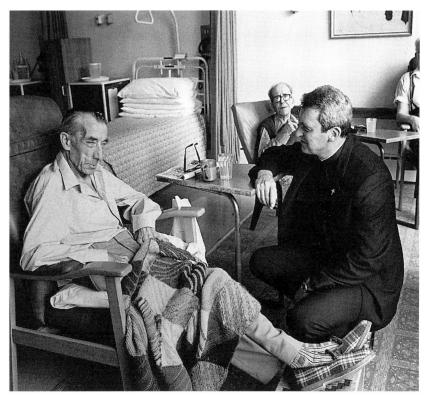

As soon as we have said 'mystery' (as we saw in the introductory chapter, see page 7) we know that we are in the presence of something that can lead us to God. How? Let us be guided by Christ.

BE CURED!

Right at the beginning of Mark's Gospel, there is an account – simple but dramatic, as always with Mark's story-telling – of an encounter between Jesus and a leper:

> *A leper came to him*
> *and pleaded on his knees:*
> *'If you want to' he said*
> *'you can cure me.'*
> *Feeling sorry for him,*
> *Jesus stretched out his hand*
> *and touched him.*
> *'Of course I want to!' he said.*
> *'Be cured.'*
> *And the leprosy left him at once*
> *and he was cured.*
> (Mark 1:40-42)

Mark takes the trouble to note that Jesus felt sorry for the leper, but immediately he tells us that Jesus did not stop there. Confronted with suffering, Jesus acts against it: 'he stretched out his hand and touched him.' A deceptively simple gesture of love.

In the culture of the time, such a gesture was not so simple as that, however. In those days, people were terrified of leprosy, a contagious disease for which there was no known cure. For the safety of society, lepers were driven from their homes, villages or towns. From the moment that leprosy was identified, the victim became an outcast, literally removed from society. On top of the physical suffering caused by the disease, there must have been the greater suffering of mental and emotional anguish caused by this isolation and rejection.

In touching the leper, Jesus destroys all these pains and sufferings. He heals not just the disease but also the damage done to the personality of the leper. Mark does not tell us how badly the leper was disfigured by the disease, because it was unimportant for Jesus. Behind the disfigurement caused by the disease, Jesus sees the dignity and inner beauty of the human person. Certainly, in touching the leper, Jesus breaks the isolation, brings him back to human contact with others. By his skilful story-telling, Mark is inviting us to see Jesus not so much as curing a disease, but as healing and making whole a person.

This episode is typical of Jesus' reaction to the suffering he met in his lifetime. He feels compassion for the suffering person, he touches them (or sometimes lets himself be touched by the sick person) and through this touch the person is healed. This basic pattern occurs repeatedly in the Gospels, underlining Jesus' concern and love for the sick. Jesus' way of preaching Good News was twofold: by his words, but above all by his actions. Often Jesus demands faith, or spontaneously the healed person declares their faith (Mk 5:34, 36, 9:23, etc.). His healing presence was the real Good News! Jesus himself clearly saw healing as a vital part of his ministry, and to the extent that he involved the disciples in this very same ministry.

For Jesus, then, pain and suffering were not simply an inescapable part of human life: he fought, and invited his followers to fight the pain he saw around him. Jesus offers no explanation of pain and suffering – indeed, he explicitly corrects those who want to claim it is the result of sin (see John 9:3).

If healing was so central to Jesus' life and ministry, it must be because he understood that God's will for us did not intend us to suffer. Nor did Jesus see sympathy, understanding and healing as something only he could give. He invites all who would claim to be his followers to copy his example in struggling to overcome the destructive forces of suffering.

However, Jesus did not wipe out all illness and suffering; even those who were raised from the dead by Jesus during his time on earth would subsequently die. We have to interpret these moments of healing as signs of the greatest healing of all, the paschal mystery: the ultimate victory over sin and death that comes through Christ's death and resurrection, and the fact that we are invited to share in it.

HE GAVE THEM POWER . . .

Perhaps we have a certain tendency to think 'It was all very well for Jesus, after all he was Son of God...'. Well, Jesus himself evidently did not think that what he was doing was unique to himself, because he specifically sent the Apostles out with the command to speak and to do 'Good News' – specifically to heal:

Go proclaim
that the kingdom of God
is close at hand.
Cure the sick,
raise the dead,
cleanse the lepers...
(Matthew 10:7-8)

He called the Twelve together
and gave them power and authority
over all devils
and to cure diseases,
and he sent them
to proclaim the kingdom of God
 and to heal...
(Luke 9:1-2)

Nor was this a mission entrusted only to the Apostles:

The Lord appointed 72 others
and sent them out ahead of him,
in pairs,
to all the towns and places
he himself was to visit.
He said to them...
'Whenever you go into a town
where they make you welcome,
eat what is set before you.
Cure those in it who are sick,
and say,
"The kingdom of God is very near to
 you".'
(Luke 10:1, 8-9)

How did things work out? The Gospels say simply...

So they went out
and went from village to village
proclaiming the Good News
and healing everywhere.
(Luke 9:6)

and in Mark's Gospel:

So they set off to preach repentance;
and they cast out many devils,
and anointed many sick people with oil
and cured them.
(Mark 6:12-13)

Intriguingly, all of these episodes of preaching the Good News and healing are placed by the evangelists before their accounts of the multiplication of loaves: like a liturgy of the Word – but where the Word is expressed as much in action as in words – followed by the Eucharist.

After his resurrection, the healing par excellence, the risen Christ renews his call to his followers to fulfil this ministry:

Go out to the whole world;
proclaim the Good News to all
 creation...
These are the signs
that will be associated with believers:
in my name,
they will lay their hands on the sick,
who will recover.
(Mark 16:16, 18)

When Paul wrote to the Christians at Corinth (written around Easter AD 57), he reminded them that this gift of healing – which implies it was something that they practised – was a gift of the Spirit (1 Cor 12:9, 30), a sign that the Church was effectively the body of Christ, continuing the work of Christ. It should not be regarded, Paul warns, as a purely personal gift, but a charism entrusted for the building up of the Church.

At much the same time, the way James speaks in his Letter shows that, in order to fulfil Jesus' command, the ministry of healing is clearly an organised rite:

If any one of you is ill,
he should send for the elders of the
 church,
and they must anoint him with oil
in the name of the Lord
and pray over him.
The prayer of faith will save the sick
 man
and the Lord will raise him up again;
and if he has committed any sins,
he will be forgiven.
(James 5:14-15)

But just as Christ in his lifetime did not heal every illness, calm every suffering, neither can his followers. The next time he wrote to the Corinthians, Paul shares with them the hard lesson he had to learn himself:

I was given a thorn in my flesh …
I pleaded with the Lord three times
for it to leave me,
but he has said,
'My grace is enough for you:
my power is at its best in weakness.'
So I shall be happy
to make my weaknesses my special
  boast
so that the power of Christ may stay
  over me.
That is why I am content with my
  weaknesses,
hardships and the agonies
I go through for Christ's sake.
For it is when I am weak
that I am strong.
(2 Corinthians 12:7-10)

How can one be content with hardships and agonies? In his Letter to the Colossians Paul explains how something apparently meaningless can be endowed with meaning:

It makes me happy to suffer for you,
as I am suffering now,
and in my own body to do what I can
to make up
all that has still to be undergone by
  Christ
for the sake of his body, the Church.
(Colossians 1:24)

Paul is not inviting hardship, or suggesting we should actively seek out suffering. But when suffering does come our way, he says that in as much as we are the body of Christ, this suffering can have redemptive meaning and power.

This is one of the reasons why the Church regards the anointing of the sick a sacrament: it is the touch, here and now, of Christ who passed through suffering and death, offering a glimpse and a share in the fruits of that freely accepted suffering. The early Christians clearly understood this: they saw themselves as continuing the healing work of Jesus, because the anointing is done 'in the name of the Lord'. James speaks of 'saving' the sick person, using a word whose primary meaning is to be redeemed; and James adds specifically the mention of the forgiveness of sins.

Just as Jesus did with the leper, the Church seeks not simply to cure an illness but to stretch Christ's healing touch to the whole person. Very often when a person is suffering from a disease, not only is there physical suffering, there is also psychological, emotional and spiritual suffering. Illness can lead to depression, to feelings of isolation and loneliness; it can even lead to feeling utterly forgotten, even by God. Illness can lead a person to give up hope, to feel that everything is useless and without a purpose.

In the sacrament of anointing, the Church offers an encounter with Christ. It celebrates and brings the touch of Jesus, praying not just for a physical cure but for the well-being of the whole person. It is a sacrament because the Church – the sick person, as a member of the Church and together with other members of the Church – celebrates and makes real the healing presence of Christ in our midst. All sacraments start with the stuff of ordinary life and lead us toward life with Christ. Whenever and wherever care is shown to the sick and suffering, already we see, with the eyes of faith, the presence of Christ: 'in so far as you did this to one of the least, you did it to me' (Matthew 25:40). Celebrating the sacrament is a tangible sign of the community's loving concern, given in the name of Christ. Beyond that, whenever the sickness is so severe, or the suffering so acute that the person seems in danger, then the anointing, a defiant act of hope, strengthens the whole community to transform the suffering into a share in Christ's redemptive work for humanity. There is another level to this sacrament, which recognises human frailty, our mortality, our death, and which invites us to see in this moment of a person's life the beginning of 'the passage with Christ to the Father'.

ANOINTING IN THE CHURCH'S HISTORY

The three aspects of the sacrament we have just identified – namely, care for the sick, prayer for healing and prayer for the dying – have received different emphases at different times in the Church's history. All the sacraments are designed for human beings, and it is only natural to find that, depending on particular needs, brought on by particular circumstances, the Church has had the wisdom to adapt the sacrament. A simple example: what are nowadays considered 'minor' illnesses in our Western world were once life threatening – and still are in some countries of the Third World. If our vision of 'sickness' has evolved, it is only right that our vision of the sacrament which interprets that sickness should evolve. However, the essential core of the sacrament remains unchanged: it is the presence of the healing Christ.

The Letter of James has already given us a clear picture of how this rite was celebrated in the early Church: when someone fell sick, the elders were sent for; they anointed the sick person 'in the name of the Lord' and prayed over them. The purpose of this prayer of faith was for complete healing, that the person be 'saved' and that their sins, if any, be forgiven.

One interesting early development in the sacrament was the spontaneous way that ordinary Christians adopted it. Just as it was customary for those present at the Sunday Eucharist to take communion home for members of their family that were sick, so too for the sacrament of anointing. People brought oil with them, which would be blessed in the course of the Sunday Eucharist by their bishop, and they would then take this home to anoint their sick relative. Here is one example of how the oil was blessed, an example which dates from the fourth century:

Lord,
send your Holy Spirit, the Paraclete,
from the highest heavens
upon this olive oil
fruit of this lively tree
to soothe our bodies.
By your holy blessing
may it become
for anyone who is anointed with it,
or for anyone who consumes it
a remedy for the body.
May it drive away all pain,
all weakness,
all sickness …

The fact that the ordinary members of the family anointed their sick relatives is confirmed by Pope Innocent I (416), who, commenting on the passage from James' Letter, says:

There is no doubt that this text
should be applied to the faithful who
*   are sick*
and who can be anointed
with the holy oil of anointing;
and that this oil,
prepared by the bishop,
can be used not only by the priestly
*   hierarchy*
but by all Christians
when they or their dear ones
are troubled by sickness.

From these two pieces of evidence it is clear that the sacrament was administered in a very homely way: it is the family, those nearest to the sick person, who seem to administer the sacrament. It is interesting to notice, too, the very natural way in which the oil was used: not just for anointing, but also consumed, taken like medicine. However, it is also very important to note that the oil used in this way was blessed by the bishop. In a sense, the celebration of the sacrament is stretched to cover not just the moment of anointing and prayer, but the very public blessing of the oil, as part of the eucharistic prayer, by the Bishop, during the Sunday Eucharist.

At the end of the eighth century, two interlinked changes occur in the way the sacrament is celebrated. The first was the insistence by the Church authorities that the anointing be administered only by ordained ministers. Between the lines we can read a positive and a negative reason for this: firstly, the structure of the Church had evolved, and whereas in earlier times the primary structure had been the diocese, now the first point of contact with the Church was the parish and the priest. Proportionally speaking, there were more priests at this period of history than there had been earlier. It was natural that, as part of his pastoral care of the congregation entrusted to him, the priest be the one who visit the sick and celebrate this sacrament with them. It was also a safeguard. We are, after all, talking about the Dark Ages, when such a simple rite, left in the hands of illiterate lay-folk, could easily slip into pseudo-magic.

The second change was a consequence of entrusting the administration of this sacrament to priests. Even if priests were

COUNCIL OF TRENT
(1547)

It is true that in an earlier draft of the Council's text on anointing, this sacrament was said to be 'only for the dying' (dumtaxat...). However, the final document is more open and indeed more positive, because it says only that it is 'especially' (præsertim) for those in danger of death:

This anointing is to be used for the sick, but especially for those who are so dangerously ill as to appear at the point of departing this life; this is why this is also called a sacrament of the departing.

The reality *(res)* of this sacrament is the grace of the Holy Spirit, whose anointing wipes away such sins as remain to be expiated, as well as the remnants of sin, comforts and strengthens the soul of the sick person, by raising up in him great confidence in divine mercy; encouraged by this, the sick person bears more lightly the miseries and pains of illness, and resists more easily the temptations of the devil, and when expedient for the welfare of the soul, the person receives restoration of bodily health.

relatively more numerous than in earlier centuries, the priest could not visit and anoint every parishioner as soon as and every time they fell ill. The occasions on which the priest would be called grew fewer and fewer, until it reached the point where the person was in danger of death. Unfortunately, for unsophisticated people one of the best signs that a person was in danger of death was that they be unconscious, and it was at this moment that the priest was called. Often, the priest arrived and administered the sacrament after the person had died.

In the way the sacrament was practised, it shifted from being primarily a sacrament of healing to being a sacrament for the dying and even of the dead. The texts of the prayers remained the same, praying for healing: but this was interpreted almost exclusively in the spiritual sense, of healing as forgiveness of sin. This shift in meaning brought a change in the understanding of the physical anointing: rather than being seen parallel to a medicinal anointing, the five senses (eyes, ears, mouth, hands and feet) were anointed because these were the parts of the body that may have led the person into sin. It is at this period that the sacrament came to be called 'extreme unction', that is, 'final anointing'.

The blessing of the oil was still normally reserved to the bishop, except that instead of taking place during any eucharist, the oil of the sick, together with the other oils used by the Church (oil of catechumens and chrism), were and still are blessed at a

special Mass celebrated on the morning of Holy Thursday. This had the disadvantage of making this blessing unknown to the vast majority of the faithful – but had the immense symbolic significance of asserting the importance of the oils as signs of the new covenant, and of linking the sacraments in which they are used to the paschal mystery.

Over the centuries, then, the idea of healing never disappeared, but it became reinterpreted in terms of the practice of administering the anointing only to the dying. It is no surprise, then, that the Council of Trent speaks of this sacrament as 'a gift from Christ, the strongest possible remedy to fortify the end of life'.

We have to remember that the key preoccupation of the Council of Trent was to refute the Reformers' denial that the anointing of the sick was a sacrament. In fact, when you examine what Trent says (see margin column, left), it says only that anointing is 'especially' for those who are dangerously ill, and not 'only' for them. Thereafter, when defending the grace and effect of anointing as a sacrament, what Trent stresses most is the grace of the Holy Spirit. The outward anointing symbolises the spiritual anointing with the Spirit, from which Trent says various graces flow.

The first grace mentioned is the forgiveness of sins, but Trent speaks of the anointing 'comforting and strengthening the soul of the sick person' – enabling them to 'bear more lightly the miseries and pains of illness', as well as to 'resist more easily the temptations of the devil'. Finally, but nevertheless still there, the Council acknowledges that 'when expedient for the welfare of the soul', this sacrament 'restores bodily health'. Read properly, then, the Council of Trent does see the sacrament as strengthening the entire human person, both physically and spiritually, in time of sickness.

In pastoral practice, however, the 'especially' of the Council's text was interpreted as 'exclusively' for those in danger of death. Indeed, the Canon Law of 1918 said the recipient must be in danger of death from sickness or old age.

As regards this sacrament, the first thing that Vatican II did was to invite us to

abandon the title 'extreme unction' in favour of 'the anointing of the sick'. The Council stated quite clearly, 'it is not a sacrament only for those at the point of death', and asked that the rites be revised accordingly. Vatican II makes it understood that anointing should be celebrated with the sick person sooner in the course of their illness and suffering than was current practice: by the time the person is in the danger of death, the sacrament should already have been celebrated. For the same reason, the Council asks that the order in which the Rite is celebrated be changed: a continuous rite is to be provided, offering penance-anointing-viaticum. Previously the anointing was after Viaticum, thereby reinforcing the idea that anointing was 'extreme', for the dying.

ANOINTING TODAY

*T*he Rite of Anointing and the Pastoral Care of the Sick is the full title for the ritual that contains the prayers and rites for this sacrament. Exploring the content of how it is celebrated today, we discover that the Church has dipped into the treasures of her past, and restored the sacrament to a form that the apostle James would recognise! It is true that the sacramental anointing may only be administered by a priest, but this sacred sign is but one, even if privileged, moment in a whole process of prayer and care for the sick. The key features of this sacrament today are:

- Through the ministry of the Church the sacrament offers an encounter with the healing Christ, and it is therefore offered to the sick. The rite says explicitly that anyone who is already dead should not be anointed.

- It is a sacrament of healing: the whole person is entrusted to the grace of the Holy Spirit, that they be strengthened, their anxieties calmed, that, if it be God's will, they return to physical health; and – if necessary – the sacrament also offers forgiveness of sins.

- The new Rite is very rich in options and possibilities for adaptation: however, the central guiding line for the order of the celebration is penance-anointing-communion.

- Since it is a sacrament of healing, it should be offered to members of the faithful whenever their illness or age is causing serious concern or suffering. It is no longer only for those in danger of death.

- To underline the essential truth that all sacraments are celebrations of the whole Church, wherever possible the sacrament of anointing should be celebrated in a community setting.

- The Church offers two complementary rites to those who are in danger of death or who are dying: these are Viaticum, 'the sacrament of our passage to the Father', and the the rite of commendation of the dying.

The four essential elements of the celebration of the sacrament are:

the laying on of hands by the priest;
the 'prayer of faith';
the blessing of or thanksgiving over
   the oil;
the anointing.

PREPARING FOR THE SACRAMENT

*B*efore exploring the rite itself, there are two points of a preparatory nature we should examine: one is a practical detail, but the other is a question of fundamental importance. The latter is, when should a priest be asked to administer the sacrament? The practical question is, what needs to be prepared if the sacrament is to be celebrated in the home?

When to ask for the sacrament

The whole thrust of the revision of this sacrament by Vatican II – even to the extent of changing its title – is to restore it to being a sacrament of the sick. Whenever the illness is serious enough to cause concern, then we should ask for the sacrament. The Church's understanding of this rite is that we are prolonging

*the concern which Christ himself
   showed for the bodily and spiritual
   welfare of the sick and commanded
   his followers to do also.*
(Pastoral Care of the Sick 5).

VATICAN II ON THE SACRAMENT OF ANOINTING

This sacrament, which is more properly called 'anointing of the sick', is not a sacrament for those only who are at the point of death. Hence, as soon as any one of the faithful begins to be in danger of death from sickness or old age, the fitting time for that person to receive the sacrament has already arrived.
(Sacrosanctum Concilium 73)

By the sacred anointing of the sick and the prayer of its presbyters, the whole Church commends the sick to the suffering and glorified Lord so that he may raise them up and save them [see James 5:14-16]. The Church exhorts them, moreover, to contribute to the welfare of the whole People of God by associating themselves willingly with the passion and death of Christ [see Romans 8:17; Col 1:24; 2 Tim 2:11-12; 1 Pet 4:13].
(Lumen Gentium 11)

In the course of visits to the sick, the priest should try to explain two complementary aspects of this sacrament: through the sacrament of anointing, the Church supports the sick in their struggle against illness and continues Christ's Messianic work of healing.

All who are united in the bond of a common baptism and a common faith are joined together in the body of Christ.

The sacrament of anointing effectively expresses the share that each one has in the sufferings of others.

When the priest anoints the sick, he is anointing in the name and with the power of Christ himself.

On behalf of the whole community, he is ministering to the members who are suffering.

This message of hope and comfort is also needed by those who care for the sick, especially those who are closely bound in love to them.

There should be an opportunity for suitable preparation over a period of time for the benefit of the sick themselves and of those who are with them.

(Pastoral Care of the Sick, 98)

'Danger of death' is no longer the measure: when this point is reached, Vatican II says, the time for the sacrament is already overdue. So a prudent judgement should be made, if possible with the priest and with the sick person, about the seriousness of the illness or condition.

It would be good if the initiative in asking for the sacrament came from the sick person. Ideally, in a Christian community which is true to the Gospel principles, even those who are not seriously sick will have been visited by other members of the parish and by the priest(s). In the course of such visits, scripture and prayers can be shared together and – if the priest judges it appropriate – he may lay his hands on the sick person.

Visits such as these would permit a calm working toward the celebration of the sacrament (see what the Rite suggests in the margin column left). This is what the Rite suggests:

Clearly, the sick person ought to able to take part in the celebration, consciously and actively. This, again, indicates that to delay in requesting the sacrament is to misunderstand it.

The rite specifically mentions concern for old people: of course, there is no automatic age after which anointing should be requested. Rather it is a question of how weakened the person may be by their age. We need to be particularly sensitive about preparing old people to request the sacrament, because many of them will remember the former usage, and for them anointing may be interpreted as a preparation for death.

One of the consequences of this anointing being received for a serious illness or condition is that a person may receive anointing several times. Such a repetition should be whenever there is new cause for concern: for example, after a recovery the person relapses; or when there is a noticeable decline in the person's health or deterioration in their condition. The sacrament can also be received before surgery, if serious illness is the reason for the surgery. Again, the fact that the sick person him or herself requests the sacrament would be a good indication, from a pastoral point of view.

Anointing should not be routinely administered, for example, in the case of chronic or terminal illness. Again, the guiding principle should be a change for the worse.

If the sick person is unconscious, or is unable to communicate the request themselves, then they may be anointed 'if as Christian believers they would have asked for it were they in control of their faculties'.

Behind all of this is the image of the Gospel Christ, who wherever and whenever he passed, was met by the sick. There should be the same spontaneous turning to Christ in the sacrament, above all by the sick person.

The Rite says that those who are already dead should not be anointed: this may seem harsh, but the sacrament of anointing is a sacrament of the living. There are prayers that can be said for the dead person, asking God to forgive his or her sins, and to receive him or her into his kingdom. But anointing is completely inappropriate.

Practical preparations

So how should the person and the place be prepared for the celebration of this sacrament? The community aspect of this sacrament should never be forgotten. The first and most natural place to celebrate is the parish church; some dioceses organise such communal celebrations, at which the bishop presides.

In homes or hospitals for the elderly, there would be a special value to communal celebrations, because they would help to create a very real sense of belonging to the Church, as well as relieving some of the ordinary feeling of isolation that residents of such places may feel.

Many ordinary hospitals have chapels and prayer rooms; if at all possible, several sick people who have requested the sacrament, together with family and friends, should gather to celebrate the sacrament together.

Clearly, such communal celebrations, whether on a small or a large scale, demand careful planning, but no less than any other sacrament – and no less, the Rite suggests, as we have already seen, even if there is only one sick person receiving the sacrament.

And even where there is only one sick person, it still remains a celebration of the whole Church, which is represented by the presence of the priest.

In circumstances where the sacrament is going to be celebrated in the house or in the ward of the sick person, if possible, the following should be prepared:

- a small table, covered with a clean cloth (traditionally, this should be a white cloth)

- on this table, a crucifix, candles and flowers are recommended

- a bowl of water will be needed for the priest to rinse his fingers after giving communion (which the sick person may wish to use also), and a small napkin for drying

- lemon juice is very effective for removing oil from fingers after the anointing, so a couple of slices and some cotton wool for the priest might be appreciated

- some families have a tradition of keeping holy water in the house, in which case it too could be placed on the table and used for the optional sprinkling rite

- the table should be large enough to leave space for the various elements the priest will bring: the small phial in which the oil of the sick is kept; the pyx in which communion is carried, and the linen cloth upon which Holy Communion will be placed.

THE RITE OF ANOINTING THE SICK

Wherever possible, the anointing of the sick should take place within Mass, in which case the Liturgy of Anointing comes after the Liturgy of the Word and before the Liturgy of the Eucharist.

When it is so celebrated, the eucharistic prayer begins with a special preface, in which we give thanks to God:

… for you have revealed to us
in Christ the healer
your unfailing power and steadfast
*   compassion.*
In the splendour of his rising

your Son conquered suffering and
*   death*
and bequeathed to us his promise
of a new and glorious world,
where no bodily pain will afflict us
and no anguish of spirit.
Through your gift of the Holy Spirit,
you bless us, even now,
with comfort and healing,
strength and hope,
forgiveness and peace…
(Pastoral Care of the Sick, 145)

In addition, at appropriate moments within the eucharistic prayer, special mention is made of those for whom the sacrament is being celebrated:

In Eucharistic Prayer I, the following form of 'Father, accept this offering …' is used:

Father, accept this offering
from your whole family,
and especially for those who ask for
*   healing*
of body, mind and spirit …

In Eucharistic Prayer, II the following is added to the intercessions:

Remember also those who ask for
*   healing*
in the name of your Son,
that they may never cease to praise you
for the wonders of your power.

The Rite of Anointing is normally celebrated in conjunction with Communion of the Sick. This is the form we shall outline here. Obviously, according to circumstances, the elements in the Rite may be developed or adapted to a greater or lesser degree.

OUTLINE

INTRODUCTORY RITES

Greeting

[Sprinkling with holy water]

Instruction or address or prayer

Penitential rite (if there is no sacramental confession)

LITURGY OF THE WORD

Reading

Response

LITURGY OF ANOINTING

Litany

Laying on of hands

Blessing of or thanksgiving over the oil

Anointing

Prayer after anointing

The Lord's Prayer

[LITURGY OF HOLY COMMUNION

Communion

Silent prayer

Prayer after communion]

CONCLUDING RITE

Blessing

Greeting

As he enters the house or the room, the priest greets the sick person and all who are present in the way that Jesus greeted his apostles at each visit after the resurrection:

> *Peace be with you.*
> **And also with you.**

From the very beginning, we are reminded of the presence of Jesus, not just as the one who healed people during his lifetime, but who himself shared human suffering to the point of death. It is the Christ who has been through the mystery of death, the risen Christ who promises us a share in that same resurrection who now offers us 'Peace'. As Saint Paul says:

> *Christ not only died for us –*
> *he rose from the dead,*
> *and there at God's right hand*
> *he stands and pleads for us.*
> *Nothing, therefore, can come between*
> *us*
> *and the love of Christ,*
> *even if we are troubled or worried …*

> *I am certain of this:*
> *neither death, nor life,*
> *nothing that exists,*
> *nothing still to come*
> *can ever come between us and the love*
> *of God*
> *made visible in Christ Jesus our Lord.*
> (Romans 8:34, 38-39)

This is peace indeed, the peace that only Christ can bring!

Sprinkling with holy water

This is an optional rite, to be used depending on local traditions. As the accompanying monition makes clear, this is not a blessing, but a gesture to remind us of our baptism:

> *Let this water call to mind*
> *our baptism into Christ,*
> *who by his death and resurrection*
> *has redeemed us.*

All who are baptised are called to follow Christ. Sickness and suffering, for followers of Jesus, can be associated with his redeeming work. Through suffering, the sick person is being invited to share in the redeeming passion of Christ – so as to share too in his resurrection:

> *We are children of God.*
> *And if we are children*
> *we are heirs as well:*
> *heirs of God*
> *and coheirs with Christ,*
> *sharing his sufferings so as to share his*
> *glory.*
> (Romans 8:16-17)

Address or instruction

This is one of the parts of the Rite that can be adjusted according to pastoral circumstances. Normally, the priest now addresses all present, reminding them of the purpose of this celebration:

> *My dear friends,*
> *we are gathered here*
> *in the name of the Lord Jesus Christ*
> *who is present among us.*
> *As the gospels relate,*
> *the sick came to him for healing;*
> *moreover, he loved us so much that he*
> *died for our sake.*

*Through the apostle James he has
commanded us:
'Are there any who are sick among you?
Let them send for the priests of the
Church,
and let the priests pray over them
anointing them with oil in the name
of the Lord;
and the prayer of faith will save the
sick persons,
and the Lord will raise them up;
and if they have committed any sins,
their sins will be forgiven them.'
Let us therefore commend
our sick brother/sister
....
to the grace and power of Christ,
that he may save him/her
and raise him/her up.*

Penitential rite

All of the sacraments are encounters with the loving Christ, and therefore we should ensure that, for our part, there are no barriers to this encounter. The principle barrier separating ourselves from God, and even causing division among ourselves, is that of sin. So the Church provides this moment, at the beginning of the celebration, when we can turn to God seeking pardon for any ways in which we have refused his love.

So the priest invites:

*Coming together as God's family,
with confidence let us ask the Lord's
forgiveness,
for he is full of gentleness and
compassion.*

A great number of alternatives are offered here, and the priest will use his pastoral judgement as to which is most appropriate – and this will not always be the shortest.

This is a particularly important moment for the sick person. Part of the long term preparation for this sacrament of anointing will normally have been an opportunity for sacramental reconciliation; if this has not been possible before the celebration, it is now offered to the sick person. Obviously, if this does take place now, everyone else will leave the sick person and priest in the necessary privacy.

One of the options is to celebrate the penitential rite after the reading from scripture: in this way we hear God calling us to conversion and our response is to seek his pardon.

All the forms include the act of sorrow and the act of repentance.

THE LITURGY OF THE WORD

At various times in our lives, at different stages in our health and in our sickness, different parts of scripture will have a particular resonance for us. Perhaps we have found God's Word urging us on with courage, when we were facing a particular difficulty; often, we have surely welcomed the words of comfort that God offers.

Now, that Word is shared, offering the comfort and reassurance that both the sick person and those who care for him or her need to hear.

Again, if the celebration has been properly planned, the sick person will have had the opportunity to know the range of readings proposed by the Rite, and may have chosen one (see margin column right).

Where possible, the reading should speak to all who are present: clearly, the circumstances and nature of the illness, the age of the person will influence the choice as to what is appropriate. Similarly, it may be better to read only a short clear passage, or even one single compelling sentence (for example, if the sick person is in pain).

Where possible, the reading should be followed by a response: the Rite suggests appropriate psalms. And the priest may give a short explanation of the text.

THE LITURGY OF ANOINTING

Litany

The Rite boldly declares the saving value of the faith that this sacrament celebrates and makes visible:

*In anointing the sick,
which includes the prayer of faith
(see James 5:15),*

These are for use at Mass for the sick, when visiting the sick, or when praying for the sick.

1 Kings 19:4-8
Job 3:3, 11-17, 22-23
Job 7:1-4, 6-11
Job 7:12-21
Wisdom 9:9-11, 13-18
Isaiah 35:1-10
Isaiah 52:13, 53:12
Isaiah 61:1-3
Acts 3:1-10
Acts 3:11-16
Acts 4:8-12
Acts 13:32-39
Romans 8:14-17
Romans 8:18-27
Romans 8:31-35, 37-39
1 Corinthians 1:18-25
1 Corinthians 12:12-22, 24-27
2 Corinthians 4:16-18
Galatians 4:12-19
Philippians 2:25-30
Colossians 1:22-29
Hebrews 4:14-16, 5:7-9
James 5:13-16
1 Peter 1:3-9
1 John 3:1-2
Matthew 5:1-12
Matthew 8:1-4
Matthew 8:5-17
Matthew 11:25-30
Matthew 15:29-31
Matthew 25:31-40
Matthew 26:36-46
Mark 2:1-12
Mark 4:35-41
Mark 10:46-52
Mark 15:33-39, 16:1-6
Mark 16:15-20
Luke 7:19-23
Luke 10:5-6, 8-9
Luke 10:15-37
Luke 11:5-13
Luke 12:35-44
Luke 18:9-14
Luke 22:44-49, 24:1-6
Luke 24:13-35
John 9:1-7
John 10:11-18
John 20:1-10
Job 19:23-27
1 Corinthians 15:1-4
1 Corinthians 15:12-20
2 Corinthians 5:1, 6-10
Apocalypse 21:1-7
John 6:35-40
John 6:53-58

faith itself is manifested.
Above all this faith must be made
    actual
both in the minister of the sacrament
and, even more importantly, in the
    recipient.
The sick person will be saved
by personal faith
and by the faith of the Church,
which looks back to the death and
    resurrection of Christ,
the source of the sacrament's power
    (see James 5:15),
and looks ahead to the kingdom
that is pledged in the sacraments.
(Pastoral Care of the Sick, 7)

No surprise, then, that the Liturgy of Anointing opens, as Saint James asks, with 'the prayer of faith'.

The Rite offers one of the Church's most ancient forms of prayer known as a litany, usually with the traditional response 'Lord, have mercy'. The whole sacrament is an act

of faith, and so the litany, the prayer of faith, can be said either here, or (with slight adjustments to the words) after the laying on of hands and before the blessing of the oil, or after the anointing. All of these elements, as recommended by James in his Letter, constitute the sacrament, and each helps to give sense and meaning to the others. Here is one form, suggested by the Rite:

My brothers and sisters,
in our prayer of faith
let us appeal to God
for our brother/sister

    ....

Come and strengthen him/her
through this holy anointing:
Lord have mercy. **Lord, have mercy.**
Free him/her from all harm:
Lord have mercy. **Lord, have mercy.**
Relieve the sufferings
of all the sick [here present]:
Lord have mercy. **Lord, have mercy.**
Assist all those
dedicated to the care of the sick:
Lord have mercy. **Lord, have mercy.**
Give life and health
to our brother/sister ....
on whom we lay our hands
in your name:
Lord have mercy. **Lord, have mercy.**

The litany can be adapted, lengthened or shortened to suit the needs of the sick person.

The laying on of hands

This element was restored to the rite, happily, by the post-Vatican II reform.

Notice how the litany, the Prayer of Faith, if said before, leads us naturally to this gesture: otherwise, the Rite offers nothing to be said during the laying on of hands. It is the gesture itself which speaks louder than words.

Prayer over the oil

The priest usually brings with him a small phial containing the oil of the sick, that is, olive oil that has been blessed by the bishop during the Chrism Mass.

Normally, then, the oil will already be blessed, in which case this prayer of bless-

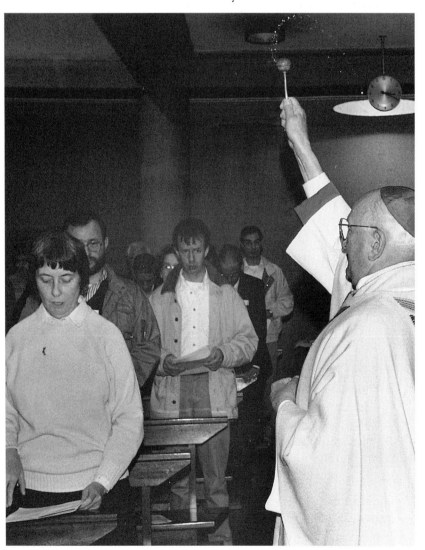

ing in honour of the Trinity is said:

Praise to you,
God the almighty Father.
You sent your Son to live among us
and bring us to salvation.
Blessed be God who heals us in Christ.

Praise to you,
God, the only-begotten Son.
You humbled yourself
to share in our humanity
and you heal our infirmities.
Blessed be God who heals us in Christ.

Praise to you,
God the Holy Spirit, the Consoler.
Your unfailing power
gives us strength
in our bodily weakness.
Blessed be God who heals us in Christ.

God of mercy,
ease the sufferings and comfort the
*   weakness*
of your servant ....,
whom the Church anoints with this
*   holy oil.*
We ask this through Christ our Lord.
Amen.

In an emergency, if the priest does not have blessed oil, then he blesses 'ordinary' oil. Traditionally, this is olive oil. However, at the request of many bishops (because of the difficulty of obtaining olive oil in some parts of the world), in 1972 Pope Paul VI authorised that oil of 'another sort could also be used, provided it were obtained from plants, inasmuch as this more closely resembles the matter indicated in Holy Scripture.' (Apostolic Constitution *Sacram unctionem infirmorum*).

If the oil is to be blessed, the priest says the following blessing prayer:

God of all consolation,
you chose and sent your Son
to heal the world.
Graciously listen to our prayer of faith:
send the power of your Holy Spirit,
the Consoler,
into this precious oil,
this soothing ointment.
Bless ✣ this oil
and sanctify it for our use.
Make this oil a remedy for all who are
*   anointed with it;*
heal them in body, in soul and in
*   spirit*
and deliver them from every affliction.

The anointing

The former practice of anointing the five senses (with the connotation of this being last forgiveness for sins committed by these senses) has been changed (as demanded by Vatican II). There is now only a double anointing, on the forehead and on the hands.

This double anointing is easier – it avoids having to move the sick person, uncover their feet, etc. However, there are other, more symbolic reasons for the change: marking the forehead and hands symbolises the whole person, who they are and what they do. Further, since this is already common practice in the Eastern Churches, it means the whole Church now celebrates the sacrament in a parallel way.

The prayer of the sacrament which accompanies these anointings is constructed of short, simple – but deep – phrases, which make the perfect accompaniment to the action of anointing. Words and gesture find a natural rhythm, to make a coherent whole:

Anointing the forehead:
Through this holy anointing
may the Lord in his love and mercy
*   help you*
with the grace of the Holy Spirit.
Amen.

Anointing the hands:
May the Lord who frees you from sin
save you and raise you up.
Amen.

The final phrase brings us back again to the apostle James, with its magnificent paschal connotations firmly centred on 'saving' and 'raising up' – which implies, secondarily and if necessary, the forgiveness of any sin.

Prayer after the anointing

Vatican II had asked that these prayers be revised to correspond better to the circumstances of the person who has received the anointing: the Rite has certainly responded to that request.

There are two prayers for standard, or general use. In addition, there is one for the elderly; one for those approaching death;

one for someone who is receiving both anointing and Viaticum; one for someone who, because of their illness, has been unable to make their sacramental confession; one before surgery; one for a child; one for a young person.

These prayers have been carefully and elegantly constructed to respect both the tradition of the Church and the circumstances of the sick person.

Here are some examples:

For general use:

> *Father in heaven,*
> *through this holy anointing*
> *grant .... comfort in his/her*
> * suffering.*
> *When he/she is afraid,*
> * give him/her courage,*
> *when afflicted,*
> * give him/her patience,*
> *when dejected,*
> * give him/her hope,*
> *and when alone,*
> * assure him/her of the support of your*
> * holy people.*
> (Pastoral Care of the Sick, 125)

In advanced age:

> *God of mercy,*
> *look kindly on your servant ....*
> *who has grown weak under the burden*
> * of years.*
> *In this holy anointing,*
> *he/she asks for healing in body and soul.*
> *Fill him/her with the strength of your*
> * Holy Spirit.*
> *Keep him/her firm in faith*
> * and serene in hope,*
> *so that he/she may give us all*
> * an example of patience*
> *and joyful witness*
> * to the power of your love.*
> (Pastoral Care of the Sick, 125)

Before surgery:

> *God of compassion,*
> *our human weakness lays claim to*
> * your strength.*
> *We pray that through the skills of*
> * surgeons and nurses*
> *your healing gifts may be granted to*
> * ....*
> *May your servant respond to your*
> * healing will*
> *and be reunited with us at your altar*

> *of praise.*
> (Pastoral Care of the Sick, 125)

For a child:

> *God our Father,*
> *we have anointed your child ....,*
> *with the oil of healing and peace.*
> *Caress him/her,*
> *shelter him/her*
> *and keep him/her in your tender care.*
> (Pastoral Care of the Sick, 125)

The Lord's Prayer

Of all the prayers we use, the 'Our Father' has pride of place, because it is how Jesus himself taught us to pray.

Some of the phrases will take on an extra density, an added meaning for the sick person or for those who look after him/her:

> *'... thy will be done'*

Like Jesus in the Garden of Gethsemane, we pray that our suffering may be taken away, and like him, we add '...Nevertheless, let your will be done, not mine' (Luke 22:42b).

> *'... forgive us our trespasses ...'*
> *'... deliver us from evil ...'*

But the key phrase should be the confident way in which we begin:

> *'Our Father!'*

THE LITURGY OF HOLY COMMUNION

It has, happily, become standard practice for the sick person to receive Communion after being anointed – unless they are too ill.

It is the duty of the community, principally the priests, but the family and friends of the sick person can play an influential role here, too, to make it possible for the sick and the elderly to receive the Eucharist frequently. This should be the case even if they are not seriously ill or in danger of death. All the more reason when the illness or suffering causes concern. The Church goes so far as to suggest that *if possible, this could be done every day, and should be done in Paschal time especially. Communion may be taken to these people at any time of day (Eucharisticum Mysterium, 40).*

Another regular key moment for receiving Communion is Sunday: this would provide a very real link with the community. When parishes are reflecting on appointing lay ministers of the Eucharist, the Rite for the Care of the Sick offers an implicit criterion: do we have enough ministers so that all the sick of our parish who want to receive communion are able to do so?

Those who care for the sick may always receive communion with them.

If the person is too ill to take solids, but can take liquids, then Communion can be received under the species of wine alone. In practical terms, for this to happen, it would be best, the Church suggests, for Mass to be celebrated in the house of the sick person *(see Eucharisticum Mysterium, 41).*

*Anyone who eats this bread will live
    for ever;
and the bread that I shall give
    is my flesh,
for the life of the world.*
(John 6:51)

After the saying of the Lord's Prayer, the priest holds up the host, and invites the sick person to trust in God's love:

*This is the Lamb of God,
who takes away the sin of the world.
Come to me,
all you that labour and are burdened,
and I will refresh you.*

Everyone responds to this invitation by replying, in the words of the centurion who came to Jesus seeking healing, not for himself, but his servant:

*Lord, I am not worthy to receive you,
but only say the word and I shall be
    healed.*

If possible, all present should receive communion.

After a short period of time for silent prayer, the priest concludes the Communion rite with a prayer of thanksgiving, such as:

*All-powerful God,
through the paschal mystery of Christ
    your Son
you have completed the work of our
    redemption.
May we, who in these sacramental
    signs
proclaim his death and resurrection,
grow in the experience of your saving
    power.*

The blessing

The celebration concludes with a blessing. For example:

*May the Lord be with you to protect
    you. **Amen**
May he guide you and give you
    strength. **Amen**
May he watch over you,
keep you in his care,
and bless you with his peace. **Amen**
May almighty God bless you,
the Father and the Son and the Holy
    Spirit. **Amen***

VIATICUM: FOOD FOR THE JOURNEY

We have followed what the Church offers, and discovered that the sacrament of anointing is the sacrament of the living, a sacrament of healing.

Yet we know that death must come to us all. The Church provides for this moment at the close of our life, in order that rather than being an end, it becomes 'a passage'.

Viaticum – literally, food for the journey – is the last sacrament before the journey through death into life.

*When the Christian, in his passage
    from this life, is strengthened by the
    body and blood of Christ, he or she
    has the pledge of the resurrection
    which the Lord promised: 'Whoever
    feeds on my flesh and drinks my
    blood has life eternal, and I will
    raise him up on the last day.'*
(Pastoral Care of the Sick, 26)

Every reception of communion is a partaking in Christ's paschal mystery, the mystery of his passage through death to life. But

SCRIPTURE READINGS FOR VIATICUM

OLD TESTAMENT READING

1 Kings 19:4-8
Elijah, close to death,
is strengthened by food
from God.

Psalm 22
A banquet prepared for me;
in the Lord's house shall I dwell.

Job 19:23-27
God shall set me close to him,
I shall look on God.

Psalm 144
You give us food in due time.

NEW TESTAMENT READING

1 Corinthians 10:16-17
One bread means that,
though we are many,
we form one single body.

Psalm 115
Precious in the eyes of the Lord
is the death of his faithful.

1 Corinthians 11:23-26
Every time you eat this bread
and drink this cup
you proclaim the Lord's death
until he comes again.

Psalm 41
My soul is thirsting for God.

Apocalypse 3:14, 20-22
I will come in
to share his meal
side by side with him.

Psalm 115
Precious in the eyes of the Lord
is the death of his faithful.

Apocalypse 22:17, 20-21
All who want
may have the water of life.
Come, Lord Jesus!

Psalm 33
Taste and see that the Lord is
good.

GOSPEL

John 6:41-51
I am the bread of life.
Anyone who eats this bread will
live for ever.

John 6:51-59
This is the bread come down from
heaven.
Anyone who eats this bread will
live for ever.

in Viaticum, this 'passage with Christ to the Father' assumes a special significance, and so it is celebrated in a special way.

Viaticum within Mass

Wherever possible, Viaticum should be received during the celebration of the Eucharist. The Ritual says that this is to be considered the 'normal' way in which to receive Viaticum (Pastoral Care of the Sick, 26). From the symbolic point of view, it is a special sign of the participation in the death of Christ and his passage to the Father. It also means that the sick person is able to receive communion under both kinds. The Roman Missal and the Lectionary offer prayer and scripture texts for Mass of the Viaticum (however, if such a Mass is celebrated on a Sunday or a solemnity, the readings and texts of the day should be used).

If Viaticum is celebrated during Mass, then the liturgy follows the usual pattern, with the following additions or adaptations (elements which are explored more fully in the next section):

- The **homily** should explain the meaning and importance of Viaticum, both to the sick person and to all others present.

- The **baptismal profession of faith** replaces the Creed.

- **General intercessions** should be adapted to the circumstances, and shortened or even omitted it if seems that a lengthy celebration would tire the sick person too much.

- **Sign of peace**. All present should take care to exchange this gesture with the sick person, as an expression of the community's concern.

- In giving communion, the celebrant uses the **form of invitation for viaticum** (see next section).

Viaticum outside Mass

Here is an outline of how Viaticum is celebrated outside Mass:

INTRODUCTORY RITES
  Greeting
  [Sprinkling with holy water]
  Instruction

Penitential rite [and
Apostolic pardon]

LITURGY OF THE WORD
  Reading [and Response]
  Homily
  Baptismal profession of faith
  Litany

LITURGY OF VIATICUM
  The Lord's Prayer
  Communion as Viaticum
  Silent prayer
  Prayer after communion

CONCLUDING RITES
  Blessing
  Sign of peace

The significance of many of these items has already been explored in our examination of the Rite of Anointing. The elements that are additional or specially adapted are:

The address or instruction

In explaining the meaning of the celebration to all present the priest is encouraged to focus more directly on the reception of Christ in communion:

My brothers and sisters:
before our Lord Jesus Christ passed
*   from this world*
to return to his Father,
he left us the sacrament of his body
*   and blood.*
When the hour comes
for us to pass from this life and join
*   him,*
he strengthens us with this food for our
*   journey*
and comforts us by this pledge of our
*   resurrection.*

Penitential rite or Apostolic Pardon

As well as the more conventional form of penitential rite, the Rite offers a supplementary form for assuring the dying person of God's love and granting his forgiveness. This optional form is known as the Apostolic Pardon:

Through the holy mysteries of our
*   redemption,*
may almighty God release you
from all punishments
in this life
and in the life to come.

*May he open to you the gates of
    paradise
and welcome you to everlasting joy.
Amen.
By the authority which the Apostolic
    See has given me,
I grant you a full pardon
and the remission of all your sins
in the name
of the Father
and of the Son
and of the Holy Spirit.
Amen.*
(Pastoral Care of the Sick, 201)

Baptismal profession of faith

One of the distinctive features of the Rite of Viaticum is that the sick person is encouraged, indeed expected, to renew the faith that he or she first professed in baptism. It is in baptism that our personal sharing in the process of resurrection begins, by accepting first 'to die with Christ'. Our acceptance of physical death, in union with Christ, puts our final seal on this process.

> **'When we were baptised
> in Christ Jesus
> we were baptised into his death;
> in other words,
> when we were baptised
> we went into the tomb with him
> and joined him in death,
> so that as Christ was raised
> from the dead
> by the Father's glory,
> we too might have new life.
> If in union with Christ
> we have imitated his death,
> we shall also imitate him
> in his resurrection.**
> *(Romans 6:4-5)*

Invitation to communion

Holy communion as Viaticum is offered to all with the following words:

*Jesus Christ is the food for the journey;
he calls us to the heavenly table.*
or
This is the bread of life.

Taste and see that the Lord is good.

To which all who are receiving communion reply in the traditional way:

*Lord, I am not worthy to receive you,
but only say the word and I shall be
    healed.*

In giving communion to the dying person, the priest adds:

*May the Lord Jesus Christ protect you
and lead you to eternal life.*

The Sign of Peace

As we noted when Viaticum is celebrated within Mass, the sign of peace offers a moment when all should make their peace in Christ with, or wish the peace of Christ to, the dying person. The sentiments behind this simple gesture run deep: how magnificent that the Church should offer this sign – especially for those who find it difficult to express their 'peace-making' in words.

> **The Spirit and the Bride say
> 'Come!'
> Let everyone who listens answer
> 'Come!'
> Let all who are thirsty
> come;
> all who want it
> may have the water of life,
> and have it free.
> I shall be with you soon.
> Amen!
> Come, Lord Jesus Christ!**
> *Apocalypse 22:17,20*

GO FORTH

The Church also offers a Rite of commendation of the dying. The title 'commendation' is taken from Christ's own final act of confidence, entrusting himself completely to the Father:

*Father,
into your hands
I commend my spirit.*
(Luke 23:46)

VIATICUM IN CANON LAW

Canon. 921 §1 Christ's faithful who are in danger of death, from whatever cause, are to be strengthened by holy communion as Viaticum.

§2 Even if they have already received holy communion that same day, it is nevertheless strongly suggested that in danger of death they should communicate again.

§3 While the danger of death persists, it is recommended that holy communion be administered a number of times, but on separate days.

Canon. 922 Holy Viaticum for the sick is not to be unduly delayed. Those who have the care of souls are to take assiduous care that the sick are strengthened by it while they are in full possession of their faculties.

Canon. 1001 Pastors of souls and those who are close to the sick are to ensure that the sick are helped by this sacrament in good time.

Canon. 1004 §1 The anointing of the sick can be administered to any member of the faithful who, having reached the use of reason, begins to be in danger of death by reason of illness or old age.

§2 This sacrament can be repeated if the sick person, having recovered, again becomes seriously ill or if, in the same illness, the danger becomes more serious.

Canon. 1005 If there is any doubt as to whether the sick person has reached the age of reason, or is dangerously ill, or is dead, this sacrament is to be administered.

Canon. 1006 This sacrament is to be administered to the sick who, when they were in possession of their faculties, at least implicitly asked for it.

Even by its title of 'Commendation', this rite and its prayers explicitly join the death of the Christian with the very words of the dying Christ.

On the lips of Christ we can read this as a last prayer of trust and confidence. However, the approach of death can cause the dying person fear and anxiety, which can be relieved to some extent by feeling the care and support of the Christian community, of knowing they are not alone. These are moments when faith and trust in God are necessary – but perhaps difficult. The community can help by praying with the dying person in such a way that expresses exactly this faith and trust. This is why the Church asks us to be with the dying and 'commend' them to God. In some cases, the person may already be unconscious: the usefulness of this simple ministry may be more evident in such circumstances, but it is no less necessary when the person is conscious.

The purpose of our prayer is to stir the faith of the dying person, to enable them to reaffirm their hope in the power of Christ's resurrection, and thereby allay their natural, human fears; but those who make the prayer, pray for the same gifts for ourselves, too.

The building blocks of the Rite of Commendation are short verses from scripture, short readings from scripture, litanies, prayers and moments of silence. Here is an outline of the rite:

Sign of the cross

Short texts, to be recited with the dying person

Reading

Litany

Prayer of commendation

Prayer after death

Prayer for the family and friends

It is recommended that the Rite begin with the **sign of the cross**, made by all upon themselves, and made on the forehead of the dying person. A simple but evocative reminder, beyond the cross of the dying Christ, of baptism, when each of us was first marked in this way.

The **readings** and **prayers** should be used as best suits circumstances – bearing in mind that the dying person should not be oppressed by too many words. This may dictate the manner of saying, rather then the extent: prayers recited slowly and clearly, with pauses and moments of silence may actually take longer, but this form of expression will be more in tune with the content of the texts.

All the **texts** are designed to speak to all who are present: those who surround the one they love as he or she is dying need as much consolation as the dying person; need to be led to see, through the eyes of faith, that death is participation in the death of Christ leading to resurrection with him.

The **litany** form, as we saw earlier (see page 94) is a particularly appropriate form. This ancient prayer is used by the Church in moments of solemn intercession, such as over the candidates for initiation at the Easter Vigil, at ordinations. By using the litany here we are assuring the dying person; that his or her death is of concern to the whole Church.

Particular **prayers of commendation** are offered for the moment when death seems near, for example:

Go forth, Christian soul,
from this world
in the name of God the almighty
Father
who created you,
in the name of Jesus Christ,
Son of the living God,
who suffered for you,
in the name of the Holy Spirit,
who was poured out upon you,
go forth, faithful Christian.
(Pastoral Care of the Sick, 220)

Immediately **after death**, a choice of prayers is offered, which usually take the form of a psalm or a traditional canticle, followed by a prayer; or, if the priest judges that those assisting are too upset for the responsorial element, he simply says a prayer. For example:

Loving and merciful God,
we entrust our brother/our
sister to your mercy.
You loved him/her greatly
in this life:
now that he/she is freed
from all its cares,

give him/her happiness
*   and peace for ever.*
The old order has passed away:
welcome him/her now
*   into paradise*
where there will be no more sorrow,
no more weeping or pain,
but only peace and joy
with Jesus, your Son
and the Holy Spirit
for ever and ever.
(Pastoral Care of the Sick, 221E)

The rite concludes with a **prayer for the family and friends**, which may be accompanied by a symbolic gesture, such as signing the forehead of the dead person with the sign of the cross:

God of all consolation,
in your unending love and mercy
*   for us*
you turn the darkness of death
into the dawn of new life.
Show compassion to your people in
*   their sorrow.*
Your Son, our Lord Jesus Christ,
by dying for us, conquered death
and by rising again, restored life.
May we then go forward eagerly to
*   meet him,*
and after our life on earth
be reunited with our brothers and
*   sisters*
where every tear will be wiped away.
(Pastoral Care of the Sick, 222A)

MARRIAGE
Take my hand

An engagement is a great event. Everyone is happy that these two people have found one another and decided to share their lives together. Everyone wants to share in the couple's joy and celebrate this very important step in their relationship. However, the engagement is only one step in a relationship which everyone hopes and prays will last a lifetime. Now preparations begin for the day of the wedding when the couple will commit themselves to each other for life.

There is so much to think about:

- setting the date for the wedding
- deciding what kind of reception to have and making the necessary bookings
- deciding who to invite
- sending out the invitations
- deciding what to wear
- working out a wedding-present list
- planning the honeymoon
- finding somewhere to live.

One of the things that the couple need to decide is how they want their wedding to be celebrated. For many, a church wedding will be their automatic choice; others will hesitate between getting married in church and getting married in a register office.

Some will decide on a church wedding because it is 'traditional', because it is more 'romantic', or perhaps even because of family pressure. Of course, everyone wants their wedding day to be special, to be memorable, this should be a 'no expense spared' occasion . . . But is that all that getting married in church means?

Those who decide to get married in church usually do so for reasons which are much deeper than simply having a nice setting for this great occasion. They realise that their wedding day is a moment of commitment to a whole new way of life, to be shared together. They understand that they will make solemn promises to each other, their wedding vows, entrusting their lives to each other for life. On this day, they set out to journey through life together. There is no decision anyone can make which is more important than this.

This all-important choice that the couple make publicly on their wedding day – the choice of each other as partner – is full of joy, excitement, hope and trust. But it is also full of risk. That is one reason why so many couples do choose to get married in church: they come seeking the blessing of God on their love for one another, and to pray that he will be with them as they journey together through life.

This is what the sacrament of marriage celebrates. When, on their wedding day, a couple stand before God and in the presence of their family and friends, they exchange vows. They thereby give to each other a sacrament, which is a celebration, a promise and a challenge:

a celebration that all love comes from God and that to live in love is to share in the life of God;

a promise that the loving power of God will strengthen and support the couple in their life together, so that, through their love of each other, they will find peace, joy and fulfilment;

a challenge to the couple to grow as people of love, to become a sign for the world of the meaning of love. This is the calling or the vocation of married people, and it is by responding to God's call to love that they fulfill their vocation.

By choosing to celebrate the sacrament of marriage a couple are declaring that they recognise that God is in their love. What the celebration of the sacrament will remind them is that their commitment to journey together in this life is the very way in which they will discover how to journey through human life to eternal life.

MARRIAGE IN SCRIPTURE: The Old Testament

Scripture opens, at the beginning of time, with the creation of humanity as male and female, man and woman made in the image and likeness of God (Genesis 1:26-27); scripture closes, at the end of time, with the vision of the marriage feast of the Lamb (Revelation 19:7, 9). These two marriages stand like bookends to hold together and make sense of all that happens in between.

The whole of scripture is the story of God's loving relationship with humankind, a relationship that is often expressed in the word 'alliance' or 'covenant'. A covenant always implies two parties, and a mutual exchange. A covenant always implies a privilege – but also responsibilities.

There are certain key moments in scripture where God's relationship with his people is expressed in special moments of covenant. By the covenant with Abraham, the Jews became God's chosen people, blessed and protected by him: a privilege indeed, but which entailed living accordingly.

Before Abraham, there was the covenant with Noah; but the story of Noah is one of recreation, starting afresh. The first covenant is that of creation itself, with Adam and Eve.

> **God said**
> **'Let us make humanity**
> **in our own image,**
> **in the likeness of ourselves.'**
> **God created humanity in**
> **the image of himself, in the**
> **image of God was humanity**
> **created, male and female**
> **he created them.**
> **God blessed them, saying to them,**
> **'Be fruitful, multiply,**
> **fill the earth . . .'**
> **God saw all that he had made,**
> **and indeed it was very good.**
>
> *Genesis 1:27-31*

Genesis chapter 1 is a profound, poetic meditation on the origin of humanity, which

sees in the very fact that we are male-and-female as telling us something essential about God. Man and woman complement each other, achieving fullness only in mutual love, in mutual selfgiving – a love which in turn gives birth to new life. Our very nature speaks to us of God as love, and marriage, as a declaration and act of love, is a privileged moment in human life where we glimpse something of God's unconditional love. This is why marriage so richly deserves the title 'sacrament'.

It is certainly no accident that when Jesus is challenged by some Pharisees about marriage and divorce, he looks to this key passage from Genesis for his answer.

> *. . . from the beginning*
> *of creation God made them*
> *male and female.*
>
> *This is why a man*
> *must leave father and mother,*
> *and the two become one body.*
>
> *They are no longer two,*
> *therefore, but one body.*
>
> *So then, what God has united,*
> *man must not divide.*
>
> *Mark 10:6-9*

Jesus was replying to a question about Jewish marriage. In fact, it took many centuries for the Jewish people to appreciate what we might call covenant love. We know it took time for polygamy (one man marrying more than one wife) to be replaced by monogamy (one man, one woman).

This social change was matched by a growing awareness of God's love for his people: there was one single idea which linked the relationship between God and his people and between husband and wife – the idea of covenant. More than a contract, an agreement of mere convenience, a covenant implies total, unconditional giving. This, the Jews came to understand, was how God offered himself to his people: in love, and asking for love in return.

As this understanding grew, there was a parallel understanding that this was what marriage was like: more than a contract, it was a *covenant*. Through giving their love to each other, they entered into a covenant, and this covenant love which they shared was a mirror of the love which God has for his people.

The prophets from Hosea onwards encourage us to see God's covenant with his people in terms of the love of husband and wife (see margin column right). With one key difference: even if the people fail – the prophets are obliged to say again and again as the people do in fact prove unfaithful – God remains ever faithful. It is Ezekiel who develops this theme most fully (see box below).

> *I made a covenant with you*
> *and you became mine.*
> *I gave you embroidered dresses,*
> *fine leather shoes,*
> *a linen headband*
> *and a cloak of silk.*
> *I loaded you with jewels,*
> *gave you bracelets for your wrists*
> *and a necklace for your throat . . .*
> *You grew more beautiful,*
> *the fame of your beauty spread*
> *through the nations . . .*
> *You have become infatuated*
> *with your own beauty;*
> *you have used your fame*
> *to make yourself a prostitute . . .*
> *I will treat you as you deserve,*
> *you who have despised your oath*
> *even to the extent*
> *of breaking a covenant.*
> *But I will remember the covenant*
> *that I made with you*
> *when you were a girl,*
> *and I will conclude*
> *a covenant with you that*
> *will last for ever.*
>
> *Ezekiel 16:9-61*

At times God's condemnation of his 'bride' seems so fierce that we might expect it to justify 'divorce', that he reject her for her unfaithfulness. But no: because marriage is a 'covenant', and a covenant of love. So we have Ezekiel's great prophecy: 'I shall give you a new heart, and put a new spirit in you; I shall remove your heart of stone

and give you a heart of flesh instead. I shall put my spirit in you . . . You shall be my people and I shall be your God' (Ezekiel 36:26-28).

The prophetic metaphor of marriage finds remarkable positive expression in the *Song of Songs*. This is a collection of love songs, in praise of and longing for perfect human love. But as such, they become a mirror of the love of God, 'love as strong as death . . . a love no flood can quench, no torrents drown' (Song of Songs 8:6, 7).

We can sum up the message of the Old Testament as follows

- all life comes from God
- men and women are created by God as equals – different and complementary, but equals
- men and women are created by God to live together in love
- through their love, men and women share with God in his creative work, bringing new life into the world
- this relationship between man and wife is an image of the relationship God offers his people: unconditional love, expecting – but not demanding – love in return.

MARRIAGE IN SCRIPTURE: The New Testament

The New Testament builds on the already well-established principle that human marriage is a sign of the relationship between God and his people.

The New Testament, though, is founded on presenting a new development in that relationship. God sends his own Son, Jesus, through whom 'a new and eternal covenant' between God and his people is established. It is only natural, then, that we find that the idea of 'marriage' is more forcefully and more positively expressed in the New Testament. The new people of God, that is to say the Church, is joined in a new Covenant with God through Christ: the Church is the 'bride' of Christ.

In John's Gospel, Jesus' ministry begins at the wedding feast at Cana – a feast which the presence of Jesus lifts out of the ordinary, as the water becomes wine, and wine of superlative quality. It is a striking episode, and the more you delve into all

HOSEA

Hosea presents his own marriage as symbol of the relationship between God and his people. Hosea himself loved, and still loves, a wife who was unfaithful; eventually she comes back to him and they are reconciled. The 'marriage' of God with his people is seen by Hosea as starting from the Covenant on Sinai (Hosea 1-3).

This symbolic theme is taken up by many of the other prophets, both positively and negatively: idolatry, abandoning God, is said to be 'prostitution' or 'adultery'. Isaiah, for example, will speak of Jerusalem as 'that harlot' (Isaiah 1:21).

JEREMIAH

The popular presumption about Jeremiah is that he is a prophet of doom and gloom. Certainly, his more colourful language is reserved for the great moments of prophetic warning and even condemnation. But this is only part of the full picture. Jeremiah's use of the 'marriage' metaphor is a typical example.

Before reaching the moment of lament, Jeremiah presents God full of affection, 'I remember the affection of your youth, the love of your bridal days . . .' (Jeremiah 2:2).

It is precisely because of this affection that God then laments: 'Does a girl forget her ornaments, a bride her sash?' (Jeremiah 2:32).

Worse, God upbraids his people as 'a prostitute' and 'a flirt'. But immediately God promises that as long as the people acknowledge their unfaithfulness, 'I shall frown on you no more' (Jeremiah 3:12).

The reconciliation comes, and God declares: 'I have loved you with an everlasting love, I am constant in my affection for you' (Jeremiah 31:3). In a clear reference to Hosea, the episode concludes 'God is creating something new on earth, for the Woman sets out to find her Husband again' (Jeremiah 31:22).

JESUS AT THE WEDDING AT CANA

'Three days later, there was a wedding at Cana in Galilee. The mother of Jesus had been invited, and Jesus and his disciples had also been invited.

'When they ran out of wine, the mother of Jesus said to him, "They've no wine." Jesus said, "Woman, why do you turn to me? My hour is not yet come."

'His mother said to the servant, "Do whatever he tells you." Jesus said to the servants, "Fill the jars with water." They filled six jars, each of which could hold over 20 gallons, to the brim. Jesus told them to let the steward taste some. When the steward tasted the water, it had turned into wine.'
(John 2:1-12)

JESUS ON THE CROSS

'Near the cross stood Jesus' mother. Seeing her standing there, and the disciple he loved near her, Jesus said to his mother, "Woman, this is your son." Then to the disciple he said, "This is your mother."

'When the soldiers came to Jesus they saw that he was already dead, so instead of breaking his legs, one of them opened his side with a spear; and immediately there came out blood and water.'
(John 19:25-36)

that the evangelist packs into this passage, the more it becomes clear just how significant 'marriage' is. There is the small detail that John makes this wedding happen on the seventh day – a deliberate echo of that first chapter of Genesis. The rather strange conversation between Jesus and his mother throws us in the other direction, forwards to the crucifixion: the way Jesus addresses Mary as 'woman' is identical, and occurs nowhere else in the Gospel. John is asking us to read the wedding feast and the crucifixion as parallel: water and wine; blood and water from the side of Christ.

Saint John Chrysostom, preparing his catechumens for their baptism and first sharing in the Eucharist, encourages them to see the blood and water from Christ's side as symbolising these sacraments by which they will become sons and daughters of God. But note carefully how he expresses it.

> *It was from his side, then,*
> *that Christ formed the Church,*
> *just as from the side of Adam*
> *Eve was formed.*
> *'Bone of my bone,*
> *flesh of my flesh . . .'*
> *just as God took a rib*
> *from Adam's side as he slept*
> *and formed woman,*
> *so Christ,*
> *while he slept the sleep*
> *of death on the cross,*
> *gave us blood and water*
> *from his side*
> *and formed the Church.*
>
> *Do you not see how Christ*
> *has united his bride to himself?*
>
> *John Chrysostom, Catechesis 3*

John Chrysostom was elaborating on the key idea that was expressed far more concretely by Saint Paul in his Letter to the Ephesians. Paul quotes Genesis: 'For this reason a man must leave his father and mother and be joined to his wife, and the two will become one body' (Genesis 2:24). Paul explains: 'This mystery has many implications, but I am saying it applies to Christ and the Church' (Ephesians 5:32).

'Mystery' as we saw in the introductory chapter, is the same word as 'sacrament' (see page 7). Marriage, Paul is saying, has all sorts of implications; but for those who are Christians, those who are members of Christ's body, it has a particular 'sacramental' significance. The covenant that Christians establish between each other in marriage speaks not just of their own loving relationship (and already that is quite something to be saying to the world!), but of the relationship between Christ and the Church – in particular, Christ's complete giving of himself.

It is in these terms that we can understand better Paul's exposé of the implications: if the marriage between Christians is to speak to the world of the relationship between Christ and the Church, then:

- 'Wives should regard their husbands as they regard the Lord, which means that since Christ is the head of the Church and saves the whole body, in the same way is a husband the head of his wife' (Ephesians 5:22).
- 'Husbands should love their wives just as Christ loved the Church and sacrificed himself for her. In the same way, husbands must love their wives as they love their own bodies – which is the way that Christ treats the Church because it is his own body' (Ephesians 5:25, 28).

Put simply, if we want to catch some glimmer of what it means to say that the Church is the body of Christ, then marriage is the key.

We are far more used to interpreting the expression 'the body of Christ' as referring to the Eucharist. Consider, then, the Eucharist, and the key words that Christ utters during his Last Supper with his disciples: 'This is my body, which will be given for you; take it.'

Is this not exactly what the spouses do, promise themselves, in body, to each other? 'This is my body, I give it to you. Take it.'

What Christ promises on the Thursday evening, he fulfils on the Friday. What the couples promise as they exchange vows remains to be lived out – but through that living out they tell each other in a way no words will ever do what it means to say the Church is the body of Christ.

And just as Christ's giving of his body brings new life, as the crucifixion opens the way to resurrection, so too the mutual giving of bodies in marriage will, normally, be instrumental in bringing new life into being. From a theological point of view, without Christ's giving of his body there can be no Church; from a human point of view, without the mutual giving of bodies in marriage there will be no new members to be baptised and continue the Church!

At the Last Supper, Christ also spoke of 'the new and eternal covenant'. All the sacraments are signs of that covenant – but given that marriage is itself a covenant, it must signify in a special way Christ's own covenant. That is why the Church considers marriage as a true sacrament.

MARRIAGE IN THE EARLY CHURCH: Ambiguities!

What did the early Church make of what the New Testament said about marriage? We have to remember that by pointing to marriage as a 'mystery', the New Testament called Christians to interpret their marriage 'sacramentally', to see their love and mutual self-giving as a sign of Christ. At first, then, the christianisation of marriage remained at this level of interpretation: in the earliest period of the Church, marriages were arranged and conducted as in the rest of society.

In Roman law and custom, marriages were essentially family occasions: parental consent was necessary and though usually the partners themselves also consented, this was not absolutely necessary. The ceremony was celebrated in the bride's home, and the bride's father conducted the ceremony.

Very soon, though, we see that for Christians, the role played by the natural 'father' comes to be shared with the 'spiritual' father. We are still in the very early years of the Church, so the head of the community is a bishop rather than a priest: we find Ignatius, Bishop of Antioch, suggesting that 'those who are getting married should be united with the consent of their bishop, to be sure that they are marrying in the Lord' (Ignatius' *Letter to Polycarp*, 5). In other words, there comes a point in the practice

of the Church where what marriage symbolises, expressed by the phrase 'marrying in the Lord', starts to be expressed also in the way the couple exchange their vows. No longer a semi-private, family affair, it is something for the whole local Christian community: it is celebrated in public as a promise to live together 'in the Lord' as a sign of God's love. The presence of the community is seen as a reminder of the ecclesial dimension of marriage: that is, it reinforces Paul's call to perceive better, through marriage, the relationship between Christ and the Church. At the same time, the community accepts responsibility to support and help people in their marriage.

The early Church was a time of vibrant belief – but it was also a time where that belief could go off at tangents and become heretical. Unfortunately, one such heresy was to cast a long shadow over the Church's vision of marriage. Over-obsessed with the idea of heaven as a world of perfection, some began to develop a double-vision, where all that was heavenly was seen as good, but conversely everything human and in this world was seen as bad. Since the body was all too human, it was considered at the very least as dangerous, and even as utterly sinful. It followed from such thinking that the only sure way to holiness was to have as little as possible to do with the world and anything that was human, worldly.

The Church's attitude to marriage was profoundly influenced by all this controversy, as the Church worked to clarify her thinking. Influenced by the prevalent heresies, many believed that although marriage was part of God's plan, sex – even in marriage – was sinful.

So in the fourth and fifth centuries we find the Church trying to understand marriage and sexuality: Saint Augustine, for example – writing at a time when one of these heresies was at its height – distinguishes between sexual intercourse between married people purely for pleasure, which he condemns as sinful; if there was a specific intention on the part of the married couple to have a child, this could be seen as fulfilling God's command in Genesis, and was therefore admissable.

These were the Church's formative years, and while it might be said that various heresies against Christ and the Holy Spirit

Father,
you have made
   the bond of marriage
   a holy mystery,
   a symbol of Christ's love
      for his Church.
Hear our prayers for
   [the couple are named].
With faith in you
   and in each other
   they pledge their love today.
May their lives
   always bear witness
   to the reality
   of that love.
Opening prayer (A)

Father,
you have made
   the union of man and wife
   so holy a mystery
   that it symbolises
   the marriage of Christ
   and his Church.
Nuptial Blessing (A)

In the fulfilment of this sacrament,
   the marriage of
   Christian man and woman
   is a sign of the marriage
   between Christ and the Church…
Nuptial Blessing (B)

THE CHURCH'S OFFICIAL DEFINITION OF MARRIAGE

Canon. 1055 §1 The marriage covenant, by which a man and a woman establish between themselves a partnership of their whole life, and which of its own very nature is ordered to the well-being of the spouses and to the procreation and upbringing of children, has, between the baptised, been raised by Christ the Lord to the dignity of a sacrament.

§2 Consequently, a valid marriage contract cannot exist between baptised persons without its being by that very fact a sacrament.

Canon. 1056 The essential properties of marriage are unity and indissolubility; in Christian marriage they acquire a distinctive firmness by reason of the sacrament.

Canon. 1057 §1 A marriage is brought into being by the lawfully manifested consent of persons who are legally capable. This consent cannot be supplied by any human power.

§2 Matrimonial consent is an act of will by which a man and a woman by an irrevocable covenant mutually give and accept one another for the purpose of establishing a marriage.

eventually led to a stronger faith in the Trinity, it cannot really be said that the Church's view of marriage was strengthened by these early controversies and heresies.

Right up until the twentieth century, marriage was almost grudgingly seen as God-given, and as given by God for two principal reasons:
• to produce children
• to provide a legitimate way of satisfying sexual urges.

Indeed, the first of these reasons gave rise to the marriage between Christians being called 'matrimony': *matrimonium* being derived from *matris munis*, literally 'the task of being a mother'. In other words, the principal object of matrimony was for the wife to become a mother.

A third reason for marriage was acknowledged
• marriage is given by God as a means for a man and woman to find happiness together.

But it was not until modern times that the full importance of this reason was properly recognised. Pope Leo XIII – the pope who gave us *Rerum Novarum*, the first encyclical to face up to the reality of modern industrial society – had this to say about marriage: 'Marriage is sacred by the will of the Creator . . . Marriage has God for its author and was from the very beginning a kind of foreshadowing of the incarnation of his Son; therefore there is in marriage something innately holy and religious . . .'

One way of gauging how the Church's attitude to marriage has evolved this century is to contrast, for example, how marriage was defined in the old Canon Law and how it is defined in Canon Law today (see margin column left). Reading between the lines of current Canon Law you can still see traces of that long history; but happily, now placed first as the reason for marriage existing is the 'well-being' of the couple.

MARRIAGE TODAY

In all the sacraments, there are essential elements that remain unchanged and unchanging. Reading the partnership of husband and wife as a sign of God's love for his people, of Christ's love for the Church, his Body – this is what makes marriage a sacrament.

It remains equally true that the 'actors' in this sacrament live in particular societies, in circumstances which have evolved over the centuries, and whose evolution has been accelerated in this century. These changes challenge us to look at marriage afresh, to see how its meaning can be best expressed in the contemporary world.

What are these changes?
• The role of women in society has changed radically. Partly due to practical pressures during the war years, women got involved in work that until then was thought proper for only men.
• Wives are less and less considered as being dependent on their husbands. This is true in patterns of work, and is increasingly being enshrined in social legislation.
• We are still living through this change, but certainly there are more opportunities open to women to fulfill themselves and their natural talents and competences. For many, being simply a wife and a mother is not enough.
• It is far more common nowadays for both husband and wife to work: many families find that both parents need to work to support the kind of life-style they feel they need for themselves and their children.
• Society has become far more mobile, prompted largely by the need to travel to find work. The old pattern of families living in the same area for generations, of there being an extended family network has gone. And with it has gone what was a very valuable source of practical and moral support to couples.
• Developments in medical science mean parents can choose to limit the size of their family, and decide more easily when to have children.
• Medical science also means that people are living longer, that marriages are lasting longer.
• There has been a growing understanding, both medically and psychologically, and among people in general, that sex is about much more than having children.
• We now have a society where divorce has become socially acceptable and easily available.

For each one of these social changes, we could pause and ask, what are the implications for marriage as 'a sacrament'? For example, if marriages are lasting well beyond the age for having children, then what becomes of the rationale for marriage based on producing children and controlling/satisfying sexual urges? If this is the sole purpose of marriage, is the life of elderly couples devoid of sacramental meaning?

Fortunately the Church has been alive to this whole question of how to live as a Christian in the modern world. This was the purpose of the Second Vatican Council, all the bishops of the Church gathered to reflect and establish the Church's teaching for today.

There are various developments in the Church's thinking and teaching that are particularly relevant to marriage.

- There has been the rediscovery of 'the universal call to holiness', that is, that holiness is not just something for a minority in the Church, something that is expected only of the clergy, the 'professionals' in the Church. 'Holiness' is for all: God wants everybody to be fulfilled, to achieve happiness with him. For most people, marriage is an essential component in their fulfilment, and is therefore the way by which they find holiness.
- If all are called to holiness, then all are called to witness to God in their lives, and the influence that the message of the Gospel has on them. For couples, marriage is the prime means of giving witness to God's love: they give witness to each other first and foremost, but beyond that, to all who know them.
- This partnership of love is now seen as the prime reason for marriage: marriage is not just about having children, and the significance of sex in marriage goes beyond mere parenthood.
- The Church acknowledges far more clearly that the family is the basic building block of the Church.

In summary, we can say that the way marriage is understood, both by society and by the Church, has changed, has evolved. Our attitudes to marriage today are very different from those our grandparents – and even our parents – held.

What can we say, positively, about how to understand marriage today?

Marriage is about a life of love

Life is God's gift to each one of us, and God's life is love. Through creation we share in life which is not just God-given, but, we believe, is a share in God's own life. We are made, as Genesis expresses it, in God's own image and likeness. But precisely so that we can live this God-given life of love, we are made male and female: it is together that we can respond to the gift of life as richly and fully as possible. It is together that our lives as two loving individuals are transcended and themselves given new life in love.

In his teaching, Jesus constantly reminded us that the greatest commandment is to love; that it is through loving that we live life to the full. It is in loving that our lives find fulfilment – the fulfilment and happiness that God himself wishes for us.

In marriage, a man and woman are called to help each other to live out a life of love: in sharing the good times, and the bad. By their mutual self-giving in love they help each other to come to know, understand and live the real meaning of love. Their love helps them to become truly and fully alive.

Marriage is about creation

Creation was not a single moment: as long as we live we are held in creation by God. God gave us life, but throughout our life, his creative love is still at work. It is through families and friends that God brings us to fullness and completion. Married couples, through their relationship of marriage, are called to work with God in creating each other.

True love is never selfish. The creative love which married couples are called to share is not only for each other. By its very nature the union of husband and wife is designed not only as a way of expressing their love for each other, but so that their love can give new life.

We are the fruit of God's generous, unselfish love. So too the love of a married couple – which is a sign ('sacrament') of divine love, naturally finds fulfilment in bringing new life into the world.

Marriage is about community

It is impossible to achieve true happiness and fulfilment entirely on our own. To be truly human, people need people! This insight was expressed long ago in the Book of Genesis where God looks at Adam and says, 'It is not good that the man should be alone, I shall make him a help-mate.' A helpmate who is an equal, and without whom Adam would be incomplete. The narrative ends with the creation of Eve from the side of Adam, which gave rise to the world's first ever love song: 'Bone from my bones, flesh from my flesh' (Genesis 2).

By their commitment to each other, a couple are formally founding a new community within society. It is a community that they extend by bringing new life into the world. Because marriage is a sacrament, we can say that they establish a 'religious' community – that is a community where God can be found, a community which is a sign of God's love for his people, a sign of Christ's loving presence in the world.

> *The apostolate*
> *of the married couple*
> *and of families*
> *is of unique importance*
> *for the Church*
> *and for society.*
>
> *This is for two reasons:*
> *because God,*
> *the Creator of all things,*
> *established the partnership*
> *of marriage*
> *as the beginning and basis*
> *of human society;*
> *and because, by his grace,*
> *he has made it a great mystery*
> *in Christ and in the Church*
> *(cf. Ephesians 5:32)*
>
> *Apostolicam Actuositatem,*
> *Vatican II's Decree on the*
> *Lay Apostolate, paragraph 11.1*

Marriage is about mission or vocation

We are called to love. The first function of marriage is to help the couple grow in love. But true love can never be self-contained. For most couples the love to which they are called is seen in parenthood. But the vocation of parents is not simply to bring children into the world: these children, in turn, are called to love, and the vocation of the parents is to provide their children with the long and patient apprenticeship in learning to love. In so doing, the parents fulfil their mission of helping any children they do have to grow as God intends.

Once the family exists, it too shares the same vocation and mission: it should never be content to be inward looking, seeking only its own advancement, at the cost of others, for example. The love of the whole family should be 'missionary', that is, out-going, extending beyond the family to the larger community and to society.

> *God has given the family*
> *the mission to be the prime,*
> *basic cell of society.*
>
> *To fulfil this mission it must be*
> *a Church in miniature:*
>
> *through the mutual love of*
> *the members of the family*
> *for each other;*
>
> *by the prayer which together*
> *they offer to God;*
>
> *by taking part in the*
> *liturgy together;*
>
> *by the welcome they offer to others;*
>
> *and by involvement in*
> *charitable work and their work*
> *for social justice.*
>
> *Apostolicam Actuositatem,*
> *Vatican II's Decree on the Lay*
> *Apostolate, paragraph 11.4*

The man and woman have a God-given mission; by joining them in body and in heart, God equips them to fulfil that mission. As one of the nuptial blessings expresses it:

Holy Father, you created mankind
in your own image
and made man and woman
to be joined as husband and wife
in union of body and heart
and so fulfil their mission in this
world.

Marriage is about holiness

To be holy is to be like God: the best way to become like God is to become people of love. The love of a married couple is a reflection, 'a sacrament' of God's love. But sacraments are more than passive signs; they actively make happen what they symbolise. In marriage God promises that it is in their mutual love that they can be certain to find him.

Marriage is about priesthood

The true nature of the priesthood is to be a mediator, a mediator between humanity and God. Christ, we say, is our only true priest. But anyone who helps build mediation, contact, relationship between people and God is fulfilling a priestly role. All who are baptised share thereby in Christ's life, and are called, each in their own way, to be priests in and for the world.

In marriage, baptised Christians fulfil their baptismal duty by being priests to and for each other. And thereafter, to all those whose lives they touch.

Marriage is the couple's way of continuing Christ's work and presence in the world; it is their way of being Church, their way of being his Body.

MARRIAGE:
A 'mystery with many implications'

Paul was certainly not exaggerating when he spoke of the 'many implications' of marriage as a mystery! We have tried to tease out the main implications for life in the modern world.

However, we have yet to turn to the real source: if Paul calls it 'a mystery', that is, a sacrament', it is because what happens in marriage, in the exchanging of vows thereafter, speaks more eloquently than any explanations in words.

Husband and wife,
by virtue of the sacrament
of marriage,
symbolise and share
in the mystery of the unity
and the fruitful love that exists
between Christ and his Church
(cf. Ephesians 5:32).

So it is that husband and wife
help each other to attain holiness
through the sharing
of their married life
and through rearing and educating
their children.

Husband and wife, then,
by the very fact of their marriage
and their way of life
have their own special charism
among the People of God.

Lumen Gentium, Vatican II's
Dogmatic Constitution on the
Church, paragraph 11

It is because marriage speaks unambiguously of God's creative love, of Christ's fruitful and redeeming love for his Church, that the Church considers marriage as one of the seven privileged signs that bear the title 'sacraments'.

As a sacrament, it is not a passive sign, but makes Christ present among us, makes Christ present to the couple exchanging their vows; nor is Christ like a member of the family, merely looking on! Through the sacrament Christ promises to the couple the power of his Spirit, to strengthen and nourish the love they have for each other. By his presence, Christ changes the 'water' of their human love to the 'wine' of divine love.

But above all, as a sacrament, marriage is something to be celebrated – and it is in the very celebrating that we should encounter and experience the many implications which Paul tells us to expect.

'COVENANT' IN THE MARRIAGE RITE

Father,
through Christ
   you entered into
   a new covenant
   with your people.
You restored man
   to grace
   in the saving mystery
   of redemption.
You gave him a share
   in the divine life
through his union with
   Christ.
You made him an heir
   of Christ's
   eternal glory.
This outpouring of love
   in the new covenant
   of grace
is symbolised in the
   marriage covenant
that seals the love of
   husband and wife
and reflects your divine
   plan of love...
Preface (B)

Father, to reveal
   the plan of your love,
you made the union of
   husband and wife
an image
   of the covenant
   between you
   and your people...
Nuptial Blessing (B)

THE PRIEST AS WITNESS ON BEHALF OF THE CHURCH

Canon. 1108 §1 Only those marriages are valid which are contracted in the presence of the local Ordinary or parish priest or of the priest or deacon delegated by either of them, who, in the presence of two witnesses, assists, in accordance however with the rules set out in the following canons, and without prejudice to the exceptions mentioned in canons 144, 1112 §1, 1116 and 1127 §§2-3.

§2 Only that person who, being present, asks the contracting parties to manifest their consent and in the name of the Church receives it, is understood to assist at a marriage.

THE MARRIAGE CEREMONY

The essence of the marriage ceremony is the exchange of vows. This is true for all marriages, even those which take place in register offices, between non-baptised couples. In the sacrament of marriage, the exchange of vows between the couple, at least one of whom is baptised, is surrounded by symbolic words and ceremonies, which together make up what is called the Rite of Marriage.

Since the Council of Trent (1563), a valid marriage requires the presence of:

– a bishop, a priest or a deacon, who acts as witness on behalf of the Church,

– two witnesses, since marriage is a *public* exchange of promises.

As a sacrament, marriage is an encounter with Christ: the Rite of Marriage is therefore always preceded by a Liturgy of the Word, where the couple and their families and friends hear God's Word, and in particular, the Gospel.

The Rite of Marriage can be celebrated within Mass, for which the Church offers specific prayers. This is known as a 'nuptial Mass'. The word 'nuptial' is derived from the Latin for 'veil', alluding to the Roman custom of the bride arriving with her face veiled.

The choice of whether to celebrate marriage with or without Mass should be a pastoral one. If both members of the couple are baptised and Catholics, celebrating their marriage within Mass should have a special significance. As we have already seen, the Eucharist is the celebration of Christ's selfless giving of himself: this is precisely what the couple are committing themselves to by their vows. In this respect there is a symmetry between the two sacraments of marriage and Eucharist.

This is not to say that a marriage ceremony is 'better' within Mass: simply that when what is celebrated in marriage and in the Mass complement each other, then celebrating both together should be the natural choice.

Where one of the partners is a non-Catholic, however, the couple should be invited to reflect carefully on the appropriateness of asking to celebrate their marriage within Mass. Very often the non-Catholic partner, out of respect for the Catholic will agree or even expect 'the full ceremony' with Mass. What does this mean, in fact? After the Liturgy of the Word, the couple will exchange their vows, promising to live out the rest of their lives together. If Mass follows, they are actually beginning their married life doing something they cannot both share! One can receive communion; the other cannot. Rather than a symbol of *com*-munion, it becomes a moment of *dis*-union.

Nor should the Rite of Marriage without Mass be considered second best. The Rite offers plenty of scope for as much solemnity as the couple would want, and in a way that both can fully participate.

The Rite proposes a variety of texts and prayers for use in the marriage liturgy. We have discovered how rich the imagery of marriage and covenant can be: the Church respects this by offering a parallel richness of prayers. To help guide the choice, the prayers (for example, the opening prayer, the nuptial blessing, etc.) have been gathered into three sets, which are marked as A, B, or C. Within any particular set, there is a certain symmetry of theme in choice of image, the style of language used and the symbolism that is evoked.

Set A is more focused on the image of 'creation'; in set B, the image of 'covenant' is the key reference; and in set C it is quite simply love that is central.

The set of prayers for any particular ceremony should, of course, be chosen after it has been decided which readings from scripture will be used. Thereafter, choose the set of prayers that best echoes the themes you have celebrated in your choice of scripture readings.

The welcome

The bridegroom should be in a place reserved for him, in the front row, attended by his witness.

There are different traditions for the arrival of the bride: in some places, the priest goes to the church door to welcome her arrival; in other places the priest waits at the foot of the altar steps. In either case, the bride processes down the aisle, during which it is usual to have a piece of instrumental music. If the couple prefer, an appropriate hymn could be sung at this point. When the bride reaches the foot of the altar steps, she is joined by the groom, and they take their places.

Again there are differing traditions for the seating of the couple: one tradition has the couple remain initially in the front seats of the church, and it is only after the exchange of vows that they take their places within the sanctuary. Alternatively, some churches lead bride and groom to their places in the sanctuary from the moment of welcome.

INTRODUCTORY RITES

Rite of Marriage within Mass: the usual introductory rites are celebrated, that is, the penitential rite and the Gloria.

For both the Rite of Marriage with and the Rite without Mass, there is a choice of opening prayers (part of the A, B, and C sets already mentioned). Traditionally called a 'collect', this prayer, said by the priest, gathers or collects the private prayers of all present into the prayer of the Church. For example,

Father,
you have made the bond of marriage
a holy mystery,
a symbol of Christ's love for his
Church.
Hear our prayers for ....
[here the bride and groom are named].
With faith in you and in each other
they pledge their love today.
May their lives always bear witness
to the reality of that love.

THE LITURGY OF THE WORD

The Church offers a rich selection of readings from Scripture (see margin column right), from which the bride and groom, with the help of the priest, are encouraged to choose.

Because of the nature of the ceremony, it is customary to invite members of the bride's or the groom's family to proclaim a reading. However, the point of the readings is that they should be clearly heard and understood by all taking part. Being invited to read is a responsibility as well as a privilege, and the person invited should be competent to the task!

If possible the Psalm which follows the First Reading should be sung, as should the Alleluia verse which prepares for the proclamation of the Gospel. Because of its importance, the Gospel may be proclaimed only by a deacon or a priest.

An integral part of the Liturgy of the Word is the homily, that is a sermon which is based on the readings that have been proclaimed, and which invites everyone present – but especially the bride and groom – to reflect on the religious significance of marriage. Given that the Rite of Marriage itself begins with an introduction which expresses the meaning of the sacrament, the homily is normally short.

THE RITE OF MARRIAGE

The English-speaking countries have slightly different traditions, which affect principally the form of words used, but the structure of the ceremony is broadly similar:

An introduction
Questions
The expression of consent
The exchange of vows
The exchange of rings

The introduction

The introduction expresses briefly the key ideas we have explored at length in this chapter:

You have come together in this church
so that the Lord may seal and
strengthen your love
in the presence of the church's
minister
and this community.
Christ abundantly blesses this love.
He has already consecrated you in
baptism
and now he enriches and strengthens
you
by a special sacrament
so that you may assume the duties
of marriage
in mutual and lasting fidelity.

This introduction speaks of:

• God being already present in the love which the couple share. In celebrating the sacrament, God's presence is publicly declared.

• The new role that the couple are taking

on in society and the Church. The celebration marks this publicly, referring to the representatives of the Church and the community.

- The baptism of the bride and groom. In baptism they were consecrated as children of God and called to dedicate their lives to him: their marriage is their way of living out that commitment.

The questions

The bride and groom are asked to respond individually to three key questions which determine whether or not the bride and groom fulfil the necessary conditions without which the marriage cannot take place. Each must be able to answer 'Yes' honestly to all three questions.

Are you ready,
freely and without reservation
to give yourselves to each other
in marriage?

Marriage is the total unconditional mutual-self-giving between the two partners. Each declares his or her free choice of the other, publicly.

There are some for whom having to make such a public declaration seems like an imposition, a constraint. Its historical origin is quite the opposite.

Roman Law did anticipate that the partners should have the opportunity to accept the arrangements made on their behalf, but there was no requirement for this to be declared publicly. Clearly there could be occasions when social or financial pressures might force a young man, or more especially a young woman into marriage. In an era when it was the convention for marriages to be arranged by parents, by insisting on the presence of the priest, before whom the young people could declare their acceptance (or otherwise) of the partner, the Church acted as the guarantor of the couple's freedom.

Are you ready
to love and honour each other
as man and wife
for the rest of your life?

Love in marriage is meant to be exclusive: the partners must 'love and honour' one another. This is not to say there is no room for the love of others in their lives! Rather that the love they give to others may not be the same kind as the love they share as man and wife.

The other part of this declaration is that the love they promise is for life. Despite the attitude currently prevalent in society to easy divorce, it is not possible to enter into sacramental marriage on the basis of 'We'll give it a try and see if it works out . . .'. Sacramental marriage is measured against God's love for his people: total, unconditional. Love is for ever, or it is not true love.

Are you ready
to accept children lovingly from God
and bring them up
according to the law of Christ
and his Church?

The love which is shared in marriage is not just for the couple. True love is always creative and seeks to share. In God's plan for the world, the union of man and woman was designed not only for their mutual happiness, but so that through their love they might share in God's creative love. For Christians, marriage is seen as an invitation from God to co-operate with him in bringing new life into the world. This is an essential part of the 'mystery' of marriage.

The willingness, the openness to the possibility of having children is part of the essence of marriage. If a couple deliberately intend never to have children, there can be no true marriage.

In England and Wales, the civil law requires that the couple complement their answers to these three questions by a solemn, public declaration that they are free to marry. Each partner in turn declares:

I do solemnly declare
that I know not
of any lawful impediment
why I ...... [full name]
may not be joined in matrimony
to ...... [partner's full name].

The consent

This part of the ceremony is like a hinge between the questions which have preceded and the vows which will follow. Again, the purpose is that something essential to a true marriage but which is personal, invisible and intangible, be expressed publicly. Each partner declares their full and free consent, firstly to accept their partner in marriage, and secondly in a marriage which they recognise as sacramental.

The priest asks first the groom and then the bride in turn:

...... [full name]
do you freely and willingly take
...... [partner's full name]
here present,
for your lawful wife/husband
according to the laws of God
and of holy Mother Church?

The exchange of vows

This is where the partners give the sacrament to each other, where each receives the sacrament from the other.

The wording of the exchange differs from country to country. In England and Wales, the civil form of words has been chosen to avoid the need to exchange vows once before the priest for a religious ceremony and again before a registrar for the civil ceremony. Against this advantage, there is the drawback that the legal nature of the wording of the vows does not sit happily with the religious nature of what is happening.

As they prepare to exchange vows, the bride and groom join their right hands. In some places there is the tradition of the bride's father placing his daughter's hand in that of the groom, as a symbol of entrusting her to him. This had the unfortunate nickname of 'giving the bride away', which made it sound as if the woman was an object, to be 'given' from one to another. This may be why this particular custom is becoming less frequent.

The bridegroom makes his vows first, either by repeating them phrase by phrase after the priest, or reading them from a prompt card. Once the groom has made his vows, the couple release hands, the bride then takes the groom's right hand in hers and she makes her vows.

Here are several examples of how the vows are exchanged in the English-speaking world.

England and Wales

I call upon these persons here present
to witness
that I ..... [full name]
do take thee, ... [partner's full name],
to be my lawful wedded wife/husband

to have and to hold
from this day forward,
for better for worse,
for richer for poorer,
in sickness and in health
till death do us part.

Ireland

Bridegroom:
I take you as my wife
and I give myself to you
as your husband.

Bride:
I take you as my husband
and I give myself to you
as your wife.

Both together:
to love each other truly
for better, for worse,
for richer, for poorer,
in sickness and in health,
till death do us part.

Scotland

I ..... [full name]
take you, ... [partner's full name],
as my lawful wife/husband
to have and to hold
from this day forward,
for better, for worse,
for richer, for poorer,
in sickness and in health,
till death do us part.

The exchange of rings

In most countries it is customary for the groom to give the bride a ring as a sign of love and faithfulness. It is becoming increasingly common for the bride to give the groom a wedding ring also. The endless circle of the wedding ring is usually interpreted to symbolise completeness and unbrokenness, and therefore an apt symbol of the fulfilment and faithful commitment that marriage is meant to be.

Before the ring is given or the rings are exchanged, they are blessed, as a mark of respect and a reminder that they stand for a love which is holy. The Trinity, the mystery of loving union at the very heart of God, is explicitly evoked by the bride/groom during the exchange:

ENGLAND and WALES

> ..... [partner's Christian name only],
> *take this ring*
> *as a sign of my love and fidelity.*
> *In the name of the Father,*
> *and of the Son,*
> *and of the Holy Spirit.*

IRELAND

> ..... [partner's Christian name only],
> *wear this ring*
> *as a sign of our love and fidelity.*
> *In the name of the Father,*
> *and of the Son,*
> *and of the Holy Spirit.*

SCOTLAND

> *With this ring I wed you.*
> *In the name of the Father,*
> *and of the Son,*
> *and of the Holy Spirit.*

The Prayer of the Faithful

These particular prayers are part of the Liturgy of the Word, but whenever a sacrament other than the Eucharist is celebrated, the Prayer of the Faithful is held back so that the candidates can be prayed for.

The intentions for prayer concern the needs of the Church and of the world, which the Church exists to serve.

It is extremely appropriate, then, that the newly married couple, with their new responsibilities to society and in the Church, should be the focus of the local community's prayer. It would also be apt to include all

the married couples present in this special moment of prayer.

The Church offers a variety of intentions which the couple, guided by the priest, can choose. Alternatively, they may prefer to compose their own intentions for prayer: in which case they could use those suggested by the Church as models.

THE LITURGY OF THE EUCHARIST

When Nuptial Mass is celebrated, the ceremony now continues with the Liturgy of the Eucharist, which is celebrated in the usual way, until just after the Lord's Prayer, when the Nuptial Blessing is pronounced.

Eucharistic Prayer

The opening section of the Eucharistic Prayer, the great expression of praise that is known as the preface, sings the praises of marriage (a choice from sets A, B and C).

As always in set A, creation is the point of reference, so, for example, the priest praises God the Father because:

You are the loving Father of the world

of nature;
you are the loving Father of the new
creation of grace.
In Christian marriage you bring
together the two orders of creation:
nature's gift of children enriches the
world
and your grace also enriches the
Church . . .

For set B, the central symbol is that of covenant, so, for example, the priest praises God the Father because:

Through Christ you entered into a
new covenant with your people.
You restored man to grace in the
saving mystery of redemption.
You gave him a share in the divine life
through his union with Christ.
You made him an heir of Christ's glory.
This outpouring of love in the new
covenant of grace
is symbolised in the marriage covenant
that seals the love of husband and wife
and reflects your divine plan of
love . . .

For set C, it is marriage as an image of God's love that provokes our praise:

You created man in love to share your
divine life.
We see his high destiny in the love of
husband and wife,
which bears the imprint of your own
divine love.
Love is man's origin,
love is his constant calling,
love is his fulfilment in heaven.
The love of man and woman is made
holy in the sacrament of marriage,
and becomes the mirror of your
everlasting love . . .

The Nuptial Blessing

Whether the marriage is celebrated within Mass or outside Mass, the Lord's Prayer always has its place.

For marriage, the prayer to God as 'Our Father' is immediately followed by a special prayer of blessing for the newly married couple. The placing of the Nuptial Blessing here is deliberate, symbolising by this sacrament the couple will (usually) come to share in this parenthood of God.

The Rite offers a choice of three bless-

ings (belonging to the sets A, B and C). It is for the Nuptial Blessing, above all, that it would be good to seek out the link between what is proclaimed in the scripture readings, and what is now prayed for in these solemn blessings.

Option A is the most fully developed, focusing above all on the imagery of creation, and seeing marriage as a blessing given by God – a blessing that was not taken away, neither by the fall nor the flood, the prayer will say. There is a deliberate echo of Christ's words that what God has united may never be divided. It also has a very clear echo of the great text from Ephesians 5, on marriage as 'mystery' symbolising the loving union between Christ and the Church. The text then prays in turn for the wife, for the husband (with more echoes of Ephesians 5) and for the couple. Here are some of its key phrases:

Father, by your power you have made
everything out of nothing.
In the beginning you created the
universe
and made mankind in your own
likeness.
You gave man the constant help of
woman
so that man and woman should no
longer be two, but one flesh,
and you teach us that what you have
united may never be divided.
Father, you have made the union of
man and woman so holy a mystery
that it symbolises the marriage of
Christ and his Church.
Father, by your plan man and woman
are united,
and married life has been established
as the one blessing that was not
forfeited by original sin
or washed away in the flood . . .

Option B is a little shorter. Like option A it concludes with a prayer for the wife and for the husband, preceded by a prayer for the couple. The imagery in this prayer is that of the covenant, though creation does receive a passing but clear mention at the very beginning:

Holy Father, you created mankind
in your own image
and made man and woman

*to be joined as husband and wife
in union of body and heart
and so fulfil their mission in this
    world.
Father, to reveal the plan of your love,
you made the union of husband and
    wife
an image of the covenant
between you and your people.
In the fulfilment of this sacrament,
the marriage of Christian man and
    woman
is a sign of the marriage between
    Christ and the Church . . .*

Option C is the shortest, and prays throughout for the couple. The echoes from scripture are almost completely muted in this prayer, which may suggest that it would be a good one to choose if a substantial number of those who are taking part in the celebration are not familiar with scripture. It expresses the Church's theology (that married love is a gift from God), but in ordinary, everyday, accessible language:

*Holy Father, creator of the universe,
maker of man and woman in your
    likeness,
source of blessing for married life,
we humbly pray to you for this woman
who today is united with her husband
    in this sacrament of marriage.
May your fullest blessing come upon
    her and her husband,
so that they may together rejoice in
    your gift of married love
    [and enrich your Church
    with their children.]
Lord, may they praise you when they
    are happy
and turn to you in their sorrows.
May they be glad that you help them
    in their work
and know that you are with them
    in their need.
May they pray to you in the
    community of the Church
and be your witnesses in the world.
May they reach old age in the
    company of their friends,
and come at last to the kingdom of
    heaven.*

THE COMMUNION RITE

Happily it is becoming gradually more common for communion to be offered under both species, bread and wine. Even where communion under both forms is rare, the Church expects that at the very least the bride and groom will receive communion this way during their Nuptial Mass.

Concluding rites

The Blessing which concludes the Marriage rite and again is to be chosen from sets A, B and C, has a special solemn form.

Option A

*God the Father keep you in love with
    each other,
so that the peace of Christ may stay
    with you
and be always in your home.*   **Amen.**

*May [your children bless you,]
your friends console you
and all men live in peace
    with you.*   **Amen.**

*May you always bear witness to the
    love of God in this world
so that the afflicted and the needy will*

find in you generous friends,
and welcome you into the
      joys of heaven.   **Amen.**

Option B

May God, the almighty Father,
give you his joy
and bless you [in your
      children].   **Amen.**

May the only Son of God have mercy
      on you
and help you in good times
      and in bad.   **Amen.**

May the Holy Spirit of God
always fill your hearts with
      his love.   **Amen.**

Option C

May the Lord Jesus, who was a guest
      at the wedding in Cana,
bless you and your families
      and friends.   **Amen.**

May Jesus,
      who loved his Church to the end,
always fill your hearts with
      his love.   **Amen.**

May he grant that,
      as you believe in the resurrection,
so may you wait for him in
      joy and hope.   **Amen.**

HOLY ORDERS
Called from among the People of God to serve

WHO IS PRIEST?

Instinctively, if anyone in a Catholic parish were asked, 'Where can I find a priest?' the person asking the question would be directed to the presbytery, to the local parish priest.

The apostles and the people of the early Church would at the very least have been surprised if not actually shocked! The word 'priest' in the New Testament is used only of Christ himself, and thereafter of the Church as a whole.

We have already explored how the sacraments of initiation consecrate those who receive them (see the chapters on baptism and confirmation), so that they become 'a priestly people'. In this chapter we shall explore more fully the priesthood of Christ, and the specific consecration by which certain members of that priestly community are dedicated to the service of the Church, to be its pastors.

Our starting point, of course, is to explore what it means to say Christ is priest, and to examine how he portrays that priesthood.

CHRIST: AS ONE WHO SERVES

When we focus on Jesus, we can see his whole ministry as priestly work: preaching, teaching, guiding, healing, leading people back to God. That ministry was expressed constantly and consistently throughout his life. But above all, that ministry was consecrated in his death. Life and death a seamless whole; Christ gave all in service, even to the point of giving his own life. In fact, Christ's priestly ministry reaches its climax in the paschal mystery, where he offers himself to the Father. This is where we see Christ in his role as priest par excellence, bringing together heaven and earth, reconciling once and for all humankind and God. As Paul writes:

There is only one mediator
between God and humankind,
Christ Jesus, himself a man,
who sacrificed himself
as a ransom for all.
(1 Timothy 2:5)

Christ shows himself as the only true priest in offering himself in sacrifice – the sacrifice of his whole life in service unto and including death. It is by his death that he sets the sacrificial seal on his mission, thereby restoring the relationship between humankind and God, making of those who choose to associate themselves with this sacrifice sons and daughters of God.

Before his death, however, there is one key moment when Jesus expresses symbolically the purpose and meaning of his life, and entrusts that very life into the hands of his apostles. This on the eve of his death, when he promises that his body will be given for all – a promise which he fulfils the following day. In other words, we can see Christ as 'priest' during the Last Supper, which we have already explored in the chapter on the Eucharist.

In the Gospel of Saint John, however, we find no mention of the Eucharist at the Last Supper. Instead, he shows Jesus teaching his apostles, in word and in action, what lies at the very heart of priesthood.

Jesus knew that the Father
had put everything into his hands,
and that he had come from God
and was returning to God,
and he got up from table,
removed his outer garment
and, taking a towel,
wrapped it around his waist;
he then poured water into a basin
and began to wash the disciples' feet
and to wipe them with the towel
he was wearing.
(John 13:3-5)

We know that Peter was stunned by this, and at first refused to let his feet be washed and had to be persuaded by Jesus to accept this gesture. It is only afterwards that Jesus explained:

When he had washed their feet
and put on his clothes again
he went back to the table.
'Do you understand' he said
'what I have done to you?
You call me Lord and Master,
and rightly, so I am.
If I, then, the Lord and Master,
have washed your feet,
you should wash each other's feet.
I have given you an example
so that you may copy
what I have done to you.'
(John 13:12-15)

It was customary to wash the feet of guests, as a sign of hospitality – but it was usually the servants of the household who carried out this task. By fulfilling this humbling task for the apostles, Jesus is teaching them one of his last and most important lessons: that the mission he is entrusting to them is one of service.

The same message is found in the other Gospels:

… the Son of Man has come
not to be served but to serve,
and to give his life for many.
(Matthew 20:28)

However, it certainly has its most dramatic, most compelling expression in John, where it is placed during the Last Supper.

THE PRIESTHOOD OF THE CHURCH IN THE NEW TESTAMENT

The purpose of Christ's presence in the world is to reconcile the world with the Father, to bring all to the Father – a purpose that Christ achieved in his life, but above all in his dying and rising again. That priestly presence continues throughout time, in the Church.

This is why the New Testament carefully reserves the expression 'priest' only for Christ himself, or Christ in his mystical body, the Church. Here is how it is expressed in the Letter of Peter:

You are a chosen race,
a royal priesthood,
a consecrated nation,
a people set apart
to sing the praises of God
who called you
out of darkness
into his wonderful light.
(1 Peter 2:9)

When the Second Vatican Council came to define the nature and encompassing mission of the Church in the document known as *Lumen Gentium* (from its opening words, 'Christ is the light of the nations'), it drew constant parallels between the mission of Christ and that same ongoing mission being fulfilled by the Church – but by the whole Church. The whole of the second chapter is dedicated to the People of God, with a special section on the priestly role and nature that belong to all who are baptised.

> *Christ the Lord,*
> *High Priest taken from among men*
> [cf. Hebrews 5:1-5]
>
> *'made a kingdom of priests*
> *to God his Father'*
> [Apoc 1:6, cf. Hebrews 5:9-10]
>
> *out of this holy people.*
> *The baptised,*
> *by rebirth and the anointing*
> *of the Holy Spirit,*
> *are consecrated into a spiritual house*
> *and a royal priesthood …*
> (Lumen Gentium 10)

PRIESTLY SERVICE IN THE NEW TESTAMENT

As we saw at the beginning of this chapter, the New Testament reserves the word 'priest' to express the central idea of the priesthood of Christ (exercised either by Christ or by the whole Church). Thereafter, we find that there are various 'levels' or 'orders' of service – that is, ways of serving within the Church so that the Church as a whole can fulfil her priestly mission. These roles were given non-religious titles (to avoid confusion with the 'priests' of the various pagan religions which were common at this time). The titles found in the New Testament are:

prostamenos, literally 'official' or 'officer' (Romans 12:8; 1 Thess 5:12)

poimen, literally 'pastor' or 'shepherd' (Ephesians 4:11)

hegoumenos, literally 'guide' or 'leader' (Hebrews 13:7, 17, 24)

episkopos, literally 'overseer', 'supervisor' or 'president', which in modern English has become 'bishop' (Acts 20:28; Philippians 1:1; 1 Timothy 3:1-2; Titus 1:7; 'overseeing' as a verb occurs also in Hebrews 12:15 ; 1 Peter 5:2)

presbyteros, literally 'elder', for which we have no current English equivalent (but from which the English word 'presbytery', for example, is derived) (Acts 11:30, 14:23, 15:2, 4, 6, 22, 23; 16:4, 20:17, 21:18; 1 Tim 4:14, 5:17, 19; Titus 1:5; James 5:14; 1 Peter 5:1, 5; 2 John 1; 3 John 1)

diakonos, literally 'server' or 'attendant' which gives the English 'deacon' (Philippians 1:1; 1 Tim 3:8, 10, 12, 13).

So for two of these levels, or orders, the titles we give today in English are derived from those of the New Testament: namely *episkopos* (bishop) and *diakonos* (deacon). Unfortunately, there is no common, current word in English for the *presbyter*; nowadays we usually speak of the 'priest', which should more accurately be the name for the overall mission of sanctifying the world and reconciling it to the Father, entrusted to Christ, and by him to the whole Church.

The first three titles gradually must have given place to the latter three. Even so, just looking at the the literal English versions of titles like 'pastor', or 'guide' shows what the early Church expected of those who exercised these 'priestly' functions.

There is another title which has pride of place in the New Testament, which is *'apostolos'* (literally 'envoy' or 'ambassador'). And it is here that our in-depth exploration of the New Testament should begin.

APOSTLE

What is an apostle? Who can be an apostle? The very first chapter of the Acts of the Apostles (in other words, the history of the earliest days of the Church) gives us an explicit answer.

Immediately after the Ascension, and even before Pentecost, Peter takes the initiative of proposing to the then tiny Church (120 people), that someone be chosen to replace Judas. The key qualities demanded of a candidate were:

– complete familiarity with the teaching of Jesus;
 *someone who has been with us
 the whole time that the Lord Jesus
 was travelling around,
 someone who was with us
 right from the time
 when Jesus was baptising
 until the day when he was taken up
   from us.*
 (Acts 1:21-22)

– that he be a witness to the risen Christ;
 *that he can act with us
 as a witness to his resurrection.*
 (Acts 1:22)

So it is that Matthias is elected to be one of the Twelve, to assume the apostolic ministry, a ministry which is confirmed by his being present and receiving the Spirit at Pentecost.

It is very clear from this that the Apostles understood that the pastoral responsibilities that Jesus had entrusted to them, they in turn had to hand on to others, so that Christ's priestly work could be continued and indeed expanded in time and in space.

Not long afterwards, we find a development in this fundamental idea of who can be an apostle; in Acts 9 we have the very dramatic account of the conversion of Saul, who becomes Paul. It cannot be said of him that he had been with Jesus since his baptism; nor was he with the apostles to whom Christ appeared after his resurrection and before the ascension. However, there is no doubt that Paul is a witness to the risen Christ: this is the essential message of Paul's blinding vision and the voice which tells him that Christ is to be found in those he had been persecuting. As Paul himself says:

> *Even if we did once know Christ*
> *in the flesh*
> *that is not how we know him know . . .*
> *So it is we are ambassadors for Christ,*
> *it is as though God were appealing*
>   *through us.*
>
> (2 Cor 5:16, 20)

This is why he dares to introduce his many letters as:

> *Paul . . . who has been called to be an*
>   *apostle*
> (Romans 1:1);
>
> *appointed by God to be an apostle of*
>   *Christ Jesus*
> (1 Cor 1:1; 2 Cor 1:1; Ephesians 1:1;
> Colossians 1:1; 2 Timothy 1:1);
>
> *who does not owe his appointment*
> *to any human being*
> *but who has been appointed*
> *by Christ Jesus and by God the Father*
> *who raised Jesus from the dead*
> (Galatians 1:2);
>
> *apostle of Christ Jesus*
> *appointed by the command of God our*
>   *Saviour*
> *and of Christ Jesus our hope*
> (1 Tim 1:1).

But if Paul sees appointment by God and the call of Christ as founding his apostolate, this 'appointment' is signified by Ananias when he lays his hands on Saul, saying:

> *Brother Saul, I have been sent by the*
>   *Lord Jesus who appeared to you on*
>   *your way here so that you may*
>   *recover your sight and be filled with*
>   *the Holy Spirit.*
> (Acts 9:18)

Immediately, Luke tells us, Saul regains his sight, implying equally that he has been filled with the Spirit.

The call comes from the risen Christ, the authority comes from the Father, the empowerment comes from the Holy Spirit – all of which is symbolised by the laying on of hands.

ELDER (PRESBYTER) AND OVERSEER (EPISCOPOS)

As Paul moved from city to city and from country to country in his great missionary journeys, he understood full well that the fledgling communities he established in these places needed pastoral leaders to guide them, to ensure the celebration of the sacraments. So we find Paul and Barnabas appointing 'elders' (*presbyters*) in these communities. In his Letters to Titus and to Timothy, Paul sets out in black and white the following advice on the kind of qualities that people appointed to this pastoral service should have:

> *appoint elders (presbyters) in every*
>   *town . . . each of them must be a*
>   *man of irreproachable character;*
> *he must not have been married more*
>   *than once,*
> *and his children must be believers*
> *and not uncontrollable*
> *or liable to be charged with disorderly*
>   *conduct.*
> *Since as president (episcopos),*
> *he will be God's representative,*
> *he must be irreproachable:*
> *never an arrogant or hot-tempered*
>   *man,*
> *nor a heavy drinker or violent,*
> *nor out to make money;*
> *but a man who is hospitable*
> *and a friend of all that is good;*
> *sensible, moral, devout and self-*
>   *controlled;*
> *and he must have a firm grasp*
> *of the unchanging message of the*
>   *tradition,*
> *so that he can be counted on*
> *for both expounding the sound doctrine*
> *and refuting those who argue against*
>   *it.*
> (Titus 1:6-9)

We find identical advice in the First Letter to Timothy (1 Tim 3:1-7), except that from the beginning they are referred to as *episcopos*, that is, as overseer/president/supervisor.

This may seem to be a list of personal qualities. However, the focus for Paul is not the person, but rather the tasks he will have to fulfil. An irreproachable character because he is going to stand before the community, preside at the Eucharist as 'God's representative'; someone with a firm grasp of 'the unchanging message of tradition', who can teach and lead the people, by word and by example, in the way of 'sound doctrine'.

In other places, the ministry of '*episcopos*/overseer' is established. These are not yet what we would now call 'bishops': rather it was the apostles themselves who were the equivalent of what we would call 'bishops'. In some passages the '*presbyter*/elder' seem to be identical with the '*espiscopos*/overseer' (Philippians 1:1; 1 Tim 3:1; Acts 20:17; and Acts 20:28); at one point in his writing, Paul seems to suggest that '*presbyters*/elders' may have taken it in turn to preside, to be '*episcopos*/overseer' (1 Tim 5:17).

However, from the New Testament the fundamental characteristics and the pastoral duties of the *presbyters*/elders and *episcopos*/overseer are absolutely clear:

Their duties are:

– to teach (1 Tim 3:2; 1 Tim 5:17; Titus 1:9)

– to govern (1 Tim 3:5; Titus 1:7)

They are

– appointed by the apostles directly (Acts 14:23) or by delegation (Titus 1:5)

– this appointment is by laying on of hands (1 Tim 4:14, 5:22; 2 Tim 1:6)

– which is a sign of their empowerment by the Holy Spirit (Acts 20:28).

DEACONS

By comparison with presbyters and elders, the priestly service which in the New Testament went under the title of '*deacons*/servants' seems clearer.

In the Acts of the Apostles, Luke offers a pen-picture of the very early Christians:

These remained faithful to the
teaching of the apostles,
to the brotherhood,
to the breaking of bread and to
prayers . . .

The faithful all lived together
and owned everything in common;
they sold their goods and possessions
and shared out the proceeds among
themselves
according to what each one needed.
They went as a body to the Temple
every day
but met in their houses for the
breaking of bread;
they shared their food gladly and
generously;
they praised God and were looked up
to by everyone.
Day by day the Lord added to their
community
those destined to be saved.
(Acts 2:42-47)

Very shortly afterwards, we discover that this happy picture has been upset, not – the Acts of the Apostles would seem to indicate – out of malice, but simply because of an administrative problem. The community has grown, is now two distinguishable communities (those converted from Judaism to Christ, and Gentiles who have been converted). The latter complained that their widows were being overlooked. Luke tells us:

So the Twelve called a full meeting of
the disciples
and addressed them:
'It is would not be right
for us to neglect the Word of God
so as to give out food;
you, brothers,
must select from among yourselves
seven men of good reputation,
filled with the Spirit
and with wisdom;
we will hand over this duty to them,
and continue to devote ourselves to
prayer
and to the service of the word.'
The whole assembly approved of this
proposal
and elected Stephen, a man full of the
Holy Spirit,
together with Philip, Nicanor, Timon,
Parmenas and Nicolaus of Antioch,
a convert to Judaism.
They presented these to the apostles,
who prayed and laid their hands on
them.
(Acts 6:1-6)

This narrative can be complemented by some comments from Paul, in the very same letter to Timothy and immediately after giving the essential defining qualities of the elders. Concerning deacons, Paul advises:

> *deacons must be respectable men*
> *whose word can be trusted,*
> *moderate in the amount of wine they*
> * drink*
> *and with no squalid greed for money.*
> *They must be conscientious believers*
> *in the mystery of faith.*
> *They are to be examined first*
> *and only admitted to serve as deacons*
> * if there is nothing against them . . .*
> *Deacons must not have been married*
> * more than once,*
> *and must be men*
> *who manage their children and*
> * families well.*
> (1 Timothy 3:8-13)

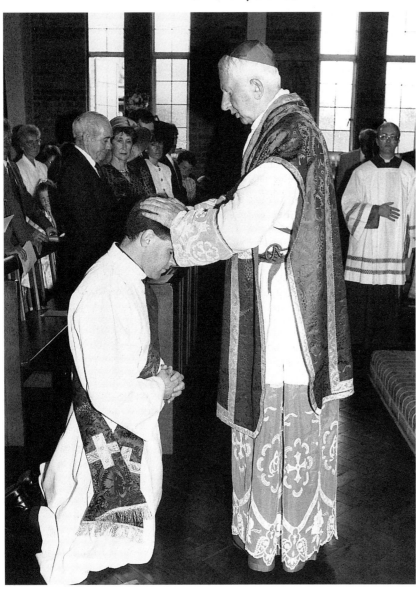

In the middle of this passage, Paul says:

> *In the same way,*
> *the women must be respectable,*
> *not gossips but sober and quite reliable.*
> (1 Timothy 3:11)

In other words, there were deaconesses in the Church of the New Testament; he does not use the term explicitly in his letter to Timothy, but in his Letter to the Romans he does:

> *I commend to you our sister Phoebe, a*
> *deaconess of the church*
> (Romans 16:1)

In the very earliest days, the role of deacon was extremely practical: their title was literally true, they were chosen to 'serve' the community, and through this service they symbolised, continued and made present the priestly service of Christ himself. By their service they give witness to the faith. Indeed, it was Stephen, one of the first seven deacons, who became the Church's first martyr (which means literally 'witness').

Preaching was clearly one of the deacon's tasks – indeed, it was for his fearless preaching that Stephen was stoned to death. Philip, too, we are told, 'went from place to place preaching the Good News' (Acts 8:4). As with Jesus himself, the Good News that they brought to the people was demonstrated not just in words, but in actions: Stephen, 'filled with grace and power began to work miracles and great signs among the people' (Acts 6:8); the people welcomed Philip 'either because they had heard of the miracles he worked or because they saw them for themselves' (Acts 8:6).

The same Philip is also instrumental in the baptism of the people of Samaria and of an Ethiopian eunuch (though the former had to wait for the apostles, Peter and John, to arrive from Jerusalem and lay their hands on them).

Deacons, then,

– are dedicated to the practical service of the Christian community

– preach the Good News

– have a role to play in baptism

DEVELOPMENT IN THE EARLY CHURCH

Approximately one generation after the death of Jesus, the synoptic Gospels were being set down in writing: in other words, as those who were eye-witnesses were dying out, the communities set their witness in writing to preserve it.

Similarly with the ministerial structures of the Church: within two generations approximately, the Church had to adjust to the deaths of the original apostles. It was at this time that the ministry of *episcopos* takes firm shape: the 'bishop' became the physical link with the original apostles, since the first 'bishops' received their ministry from the apostles (by laying on of hands). They in turn, entrusted the same ministry to others. In the Creed the Church declares itself to be 'apostolic': the bishops are the guarantors of this apostolicity. Today's bishops are together seen to be the successors of the apostles; in addition, each bishop is the 'apostle' for his own local community.

Saint Ignatius of Antioch, around AD 100, wrote to the Church at Smyrna to tell them:

> *No one should do anything
> that pertains to the Church
> without the bishop's permission.
> The only proper eucharist is one
> celebrated by the Bishop
> or one of his representatives.*
> (Letter to the Smyrnaeans, VIII)

The early Christian communities grew up in the towns, and the pastoral life of these communities was built around the bishop, assisted by his 'presbyters' and deacons. In our exploration of the history of confirmation, for example, we saw how the bishop presided over the single continuous rite of baptising, anointing and imposing hands, followed by the Eucharist.

Constantine's conversion to Christianity and his making it the official religion of his Empire was to launch a period of growth in the Church. This growth was both numerical and geographical. Where the Church previously existed in small numbers, there were now many more; and whereas before the Church had been essentially town-based, it now spread out into the countryside. This growth did not happen overnight, but as it took place, the bishop found that instead of being the pastor to a couple of hundred people all centred around the cathedral, he was now responsible for thousands, spread far more widely. It became physically impossible for the bishop to preside at a eucharist for all of his people.

Already, while there was still a single celebration, the different levels or orders of ministers had played different roles: for example, in initiation: the deacons and deaconesses had a specific role during the water rite of baptism; the immersion was administered by a presbyter, at the font, while the bishop remained at his *cathedra*, his episcopal throne; when the newly baptised were led back, into the main part of the church, now clothed in white, the bishop imposed his hands on them and gave them the sign of peace. As far back as New Testament times, it was the presbyters who administered the sacrament of anointing to the sick (see pages 87).

Here, then, was a ready-made pastoral solution to the problem of how to ensure the celebration of sacraments in the growing Church: different roles were already ascribed within a single building. The differentiation of roles was simply extended, so that they were now fulfilled in the multiplicity of churches that were now being built.

So from the fifth century we find presbyters assuming the pastoral function of 'mini-bishops': the bishop remained the head of the local church, but he delegated presbyters to preside at the Eucharist, to baptise and make the first post-baptismal anointing. At this stage it was still the bishop alone who presided over the reconciliation of penitents (which took place during the last Mass celebrated before the Easter Vigil, namely Holy Thursday – see page 69); it was still the bishop who completed the process of initiation by the final anointing and laying on of hands (see the chapter on confirmation, especially pages 34-36). However, in everyday Christian life, and for the Sunday celebration of the Eucharist, the basic community was centred around the presbyter: so the 'parish'

ONE SACRAMENT: THREE 'ORDERS'

There is one sacrament of ordination, but there are three distinct rites: this is because the 'priestly' ministry is shared among bishops, priests and deacons. Therefore we speak of orders in the plural. Here is how the Catechism explains the origin of our English expression 'orders'.

The word *order* in Roman antiquity designated an established civil body, especially a governing body. *Ordinatio* means incorporation into an *ordo*. In the Church there are established bodies which Tradition, not without a basis in Sacred Scripture (Heb 5:6, 7:11; Ps 110:4), has since ancient times called *taxeis* (Greek) or *ordines*. And so the liturgy speaks of the *ordo episcoporum*, the *ordo presbyterorum*, the *ordo diaconorum*. Other groups also receive this name of *ordo*: catechumens, virgins, spouses, widows . . .

Integration into one of these bodies in the Church was accomplished by a rite called *ordinatio*, a religious and liturgical act which was a consecration, a blessing or a sacrament. Today the word 'ordination' is reserved for the sacramental act which integrates a man into the order of bishops, presbyters, or deacons, and goes beyond a simple *election, designation, delegation,* or *institution* by the community, for it confers a gift of the Holy Spirit that permits the exercise of a 'sacred power' (*sacra potestas*) [cf. Lumen Gentium, 10] which can come only from Christ himself through his Church. Ordination is also called *consecratio*, for it is a setting apart and an investiture by Christ himself for his Church. The *laying on of hands* by the bishop, with the consecratory prayer, constitutes the visible sign of this ordination.

Catechism 1537-38

For DEACONS

Numbers 3:5-9
*The Levites are at
the service of Aaron*

Acts 6:1-7
*The Twelve appoint
the first deacons*

Acts 8:26-40
The ministry of Philip, the deacon

1 Timothy 3:8-10, 12-13
The qualities required of deacons

For PRIESTS

Numbers 11:11-25
*Elders, filled with the spirit,
to share the burden of the people*

For BISHOPS

1 Timothy 4:12b-16
You have a spiritual gift in you

2 Timothy 1:6-14
*Fan into a flame the gift
that God gave you*

For BISHOPS and PRIESTS

Isaiah 61:1-3a
*The Lord has anointed me
and sent me*

Acts 20:17-36
*Keep watch over the flock
of which the Spirit
has made you overseers*

At any ordination

Jeremiah 1:4-9
*Go now to those
to whom I send you*

Acts 10:37-43
*We can witness to
eveything Jesus did*

Romans 12:4-8
*Our gifts differ according to
the grace given to us*

2 Corinthians 4:1-2, 5-7
Your servants, for Jesus' sake

2 Corinthians 5:14-20
*The work of handing on
reconciliation*

was born. The bishop remained the chief pastor, and the community for which he was responsible was the diocese. For each diocese there was a 'cathedral', that is, one church where the bishop had his official seat of office, his '*cathedra*' the chair from which he acted as 'apostle' for the community.

Gradually the terminology changed: because the person who fulfilled the closer and more obvious 'priestly' role was the presbyter, he began to be called 'priest'. The pastoral restructuring also led to a decline in the role of the deacon. Indeed, the ministry of deacon almost completely disappeared. It survived in the form of a first stage of orders, through which those preparing for ordination to the priesthood passed as part of their preparation.

OUTLINE

We speak of the sacrament of 'orders', because there are three: deacon, priest and bishop (see margin column on page 127). However, it is one sacrament and it should therefore come as no surprise that the structure of each ordination rite is essentially the same.

At the bottom of the page is an outline, showing the parallels between the three rites.

The sacrament of ordination is always celebrated within Mass. Indeed, all the sacraments (except the sacrament of penance) can and should wherever possible be celebrated within Mass. However, since part of the essence of the 'order' to which a deacon, a priest or bishop is consecrated includes a specifically liturgical service, exercised within Mass, the rite of ordination is always followed by the liturgy of the Eucharist.

Since the candidates are called from among the people of God to serve them, the sacrament should be celebrated on a day, at a time and in a place when a large number of the faithful can be present.

DEACON	PRIEST	BISHOP
LITURGY OF THE WORD	LITURGY OF THE WORD	LITURGY OF THE WORD
ORDINATION OF DEACONS	ORDINATION OF PRIESTS	ORDINATION OF A BISHOP
Calling of the candidates	Calling of the candidates	Hymn
Presentation of the candidates	Presentation of the candidates	Presentation of the bishop-elect
Election by the bishop	Election by the bishop	Apostolic Letter
and consent of the people	and consent of the people	and consent of the people
Homily	Homily	Homily
[Commitment to celibacy]	[Commitment to celibacy]	
Examination of the candidates	Examination of the candidates	Examination of the candidate
Promise of obedience	Promise of obedience	
Invitation to prayer and	Invitation to prayer and	Invitation to prayer and
Litany of the saints	Litany of the saints	Litany of the saints
Laying on of hands	Laying on of hands	Laying on of hands
		Book of the Gospels
Prayer of consecration	Prayer of consecration	Prayer of consecration
		Anointing of the bishop's head
		Presentation of the Book of the Gospels
Investiture (stole and dalmatic)	Investiture (stole and chasuble)	Investiture (stole and dalmatic)
	Anointing of hands	
Presentation of the Book of the Gospels	Presentation of the Gifts	
		Seating of the bishop
Kiss of peace	Kiss of peace	Kiss of peace
LITURGY OF THE EUCHARIST	LITURGY OF THE EUCHARIST	LITURGY OF THE EUCHARIST

Ideally, ordination – which can only be administered by a bishop – should take place at the *cathedra*, at the bishop's chair. However, it may also take place in the candidate's own parish.

If the candidate is a deacon, he wears an alb (symbol of the white garment of baptism); if he is already a deacon and is to be ordained a priest, he wears the alb and the deacon's stole. A bishop-elect wears all the priestly vestments, plus a dalmatic and a pectoral cross.

A deacon or a priest is (usually) called and ordained by one bishop, the bishop whose diocese he will serve. For the ordination of a bishop, however, three consecrating bishops are required. This is both a symbol and a safeguard of the unity among the local churches: the agreement of two other bishops from other dioceses (from other churches) is needed:

> The character and collegial nature of the episcopal order are evidenced among other ways by the Church's ancient practice which calls for several bishops to participate in the consecration of a new bishop. (Catechism 1559)

THE LITURGY OF THE WORD

The readings may be taken in part or in whole from the Mass of the day, or from the texts proposed by the Rite of ordination (see margin columns left and right).

The profession of faith is not recited, nor is the Prayer of the Faithful said. Immediately after the Gospel, the Rite of Ordination begins.

RITE OF ORDINATION

At the ordination of a bishop the rite is introduced by the singing of the hymn, *Veni, Creator Spiritus* (or a similar hymn). The power of the Holy Spirit and all his gifts is immediately evoked by the whole assembly.

Presentation of candidates

For **deacons or priests**, the candidate is called forward by the deacon who assists the consecrating bishop:

> Let . . . . . who is to be ordained
> deacon/priest
> please come forward.

The bishop asks:

> Do you judge him to be worthy?

The presenting deacon replies:

> After enquiry among the people of
> Christ
> and upon recommendation of those
> concerned with his training,
> I testify that he has been found worthy.

For a **bishop**, the candidate is presented by one of the priests, who says to the consecrating bishop:

> Most Reverend Father,
> the Church of . . . . . [naming the
> diocese]
> asks you to ordain this priest . . . . .
> for service as bishop.

Apostolic letter*

[*for BISHOP only]

In the Roman Rite, a bishop cannot be ordained without the explicit consent of the Bishop of Rome:

> In our day, the lawful ordination of a
> bishop requires a special
> intervention of the Bishop of Rome,
> because he is the supreme visible
> bond of the communion of the
> particular Churches in the one
> Church and the guarantor of their
> freedom.
> (Catechism 1559)

Which is why Canon Law stipulates:

> No Bishop is permitted to consecrate
> anyone as Bishop, unless it is first
> established that a pontifical
> mandate has been issued.

(Canon 1013)

So, at this moment in the rite the consecrating bishop asks:

> Have you the mandates from the
> Holy See?

SCRIPTURE READINGS FOR ORDINATION
(continued)

Ephesians 4:1-7, 11-13
*In the work of service,
building up the body of Christ*

1 Timothy 4:12-16
You have a spiritual gift

Hebrews 5:1-10
*Christ acclaimed by God
as high priest*

1 Peter 4:7b-11
*Stewards responsible for the
different graces of God*

1 Peter 5:1-4
*Be shepherds of the flock of God
that is entrusted to you*

Matthew 5:13-16
You are the light of the world

Matthew 9:35-38
*Ask the Lord of the harvest
to send labourers*

Matthew 10:1-5a
*The Twelve are chosen
and sent out*

Matthew 20:25-28
*Anyone who wants to be first
must be your servant*

Luke 10:1-9
*The harvest is rich
but the labourers few*

Luke 12:35-44
*Happy the servants the Master
finds awake*

Luke 22:14-20, 24-30
Do this as a memorial of me

John 10:11-18
*The good shepherd lays down
his life for his sheep*

John 12:24-26
*If a man serves me,
he must follow me*

John 15:9-17
*You did not choose me,
I chose you*

John 17:6, 14-10
I consecrate myself for their sake

John 20:19-23
*As the Father sent me,
I am sending you*

John 21:15-17
Feed my lambs, feed my sheep

And having received the assurance that these have been received, he asks that these documents be read.

Election by the Bishop*

*[*for DEACON and PRIEST only]*

The bishop says:

*We rely on the help of the Lord God
and our Saviour Jesus Christ,
and we choose this man, our brother,*
[either] *for the order of deacons,*
[or] *for priesthood in the
presbyteral order.*

Consent of the people

The people give their consent to the election of the candidate for diaconal or priestly ordination by replying to the bishop:

Thanks be to God.

This assent to the bishop's choice can be expressed in some other, fuller but appropriate way.

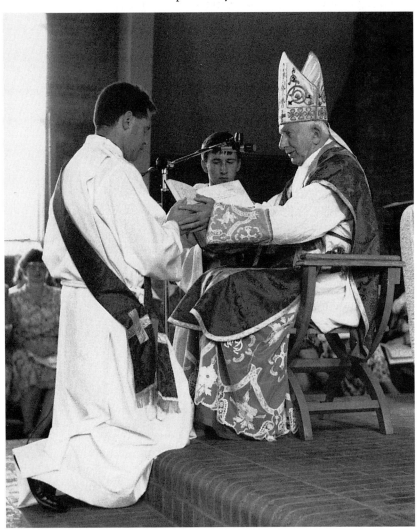

Similarly for the ordination of a bishop, after the reading of the Apostolic Mandate.

The significance of these rites is that the bishop, the head of the local church, voices aloud 'the vocation', the call of the candidate. The call comes from Christ, and it is voiced on Christ's behalf by the bishop. Moreover, the call from Christ is always to a particular service, to a particular community. The bishop, in the name of the community, chooses the candidates as one who will serve it.

For the ordination of a bishop, this election moves to another level, to that of the level of the 'college' of bishops. Each diocese is a full church and the bishops collectively are successors to the apostles:

*The order of bishops is the successor to
the college of the apostles in teaching
authority and pastoral rule; or
rather, in the episcopal order, the
apostolic body continues without a
break.*
(Lumen Gentium 22)

They constitute one apostolic college, under the successor of Peter.

*The college of bishops has no authority
unless it is simultaneously conceived
of in terms of its head.*
(Lumen Gentium 22)

This is symbolised by the Apostolic Mandate, which is the letter from the Bishop of Rome, authorising the bishop's ordination.

Homily

The consecrating bishop now explains the meaning of ordination and the service to which it consecrates the recipient. The first part is addressed to the whole assembly; the second to the candidate. The Bishop may express this in his own words, but the Rite suggests what needs to be said.

At the ordination of a deacon, for the assembly:

*He will draw new strength from the
gift of the Holy Spirit.
He will help the bishop and his body
of priests
as a minister of the word, of the altar,
and of charity.*

He will make himself a servant to all.
As a minister of the altar he will
*   proclaim the Gospel,*
and give the Lord's body and blood to
*   the community of believers.*
It will also be his duty, at the bishop's
*   discretion,*
to bring God's word to believer and
*   unbeliever alike,*
to preside over public prayer,
to baptise,
to assist at marriages and bless them,
to give viaticum to the dying,
and to lead the rites of burial.
Once he is consecrated by the laying on
*   of hands*
that comes to us from the apostles
and is more closely bound to the altar,
he will perform works of charity in the
*   name of the bishop or pastor.*
From the way he goes about these
*   duties,*
may you recognise him as a disciple of
*   Jesus,*
who came to serve, not to be served.

And to the candidate:

The Lord has set an example for you to
*   follow.*
As a deacon you will serve Jesus Christ,
who was known among his disciples
as the one who served others.
Do the will of God generously.
Serve God and mankind in love and
*   joy.*
Look upon all unchastity and avarice
*   as worship of false gods;*
for no man can serve two masters.
Like the men the apostles chose for
*   works of charity,*
you should be a man of good
*   reputation,*
filled with wisdom and the Holy
*   Spirit.*
Show before God and mankind
that you are above every suspicion of
*   blame,*
a true minister of Christ and of God's
*   mysteries,*
a man firmly rooted in faith.
Never turn away from the hope which
*   the Gospel offers;*
now you must not only listen to God's
*   word*
but also preach it.
Hold the mystery of faith with a clear

conscience.
Express in action what you proclaim
*   by word of mouth.*
Then the people of Christ,
brought to life in the Spirit,
will be an offering God accepts.
Finally, on the last day,
when you go to meet the Lord,
you will hear him say:
'Well done, good and faithful servant,
enter into the joy of your Lord.'

At the ordination of a priest, for the
assembly:

It is true that God has made his entire
*   people a royal priesthood in Christ.*
But our High Priest, Jesus Christ,
also chose some of his followers to carry
*   out publicly in the Church*
a priestly ministry
in his name on behalf of mankind.
He was sent by the Father,
and he in turn sent the apostles into
*   the world;*
through them and their successors, the
*   bishops,*
he continues his work as Teacher,
*   Priest and Shepherd.*
Priest are co-workers of the order of
*   bishops.*
They are joined to the bishops in the
*   priestly office*
and are called to serve God's people.
Our brother has seriously considered
*   this step*
and is now to be ordained to
*   priesthood in the presbyteral order.*
He is to serve Christ the Teacher, Priest
*   and Shepherd in his ministry*
which is to make his own body, the
*   Church,*
grow into the people of God, a holy
*   temple.*
He is called to share in the priesthood
*   of the bishops*
and to be modelled into the likeness of
*   Christ,*
the supreme and eternal Priest.
By consecration he will be made a true
*   priest of the New Testament,*
to preach the Gospel,
sustain God's people,
and celebrate the liturgy,
above all, the Lord's sacrifice.

And to the candidate:

You are now to be advanced to the
order of the presbyterate.
You must apply your energies
to the duty of teaching in the name of
Christ, the chief Teacher.
Share with all mankind the word of
God
you have received with joy.
Meditate on the law of God,
believe what you read,
teach what you believe,
and put into practice what you teach.
Let the doctrine you teach be true
nourishment for the people of God.
Let the example of your life attract the
followers of Christ,
so that by word and action
you may build up the house which is
God's Church.
In the same way
you must carry out your mission of
sanctifying in the power of Christ.
Your ministry will perfect the spiritual
sacrifice of the faithful
by uniting it to Christ's sacrifice,
the sacrifice which is offered
sacramentally through your hands.
Know what you are doing
and imitate the mysteries you celebrate.
In the memorial of the Lord's death
and resurrection,
make every effort to die to sin
and to walk in the new life of Christ.
When you baptise,
you will bring men and women into
the people of God.
In the sacrament of penance,
you will forgive sins in the name of
Christ and the Church.
With holy oil you will relieve and
console the sick.
You will celebrate the liturgy
and offer praise and thanksgiving to
God throughout the day,
praying not only for the people of God
but for the whole world.
Remember that you are chosen from
among God's people
and appointed to act for them in
relation to God.
Do your part in the work of Christ the
Priest
with genuine joy and love,
and attend to the concerns of Christ
before your own.
Finally, conscious of sharing in the
work of Christ,
the Head and Shepherd of the Church,
and united with the bishop and
subject to him,
seek to bring the faithful together into
a unified family
and to lead them effectively,
through Christ and in the Holy Spirit,
to God the Father.
Always remember the example of
Christ the Good Shepherd
who came not to be served but to serve,
and to seek out and rescue those who
were lost.

At the ordination of a bishop, for the assembly:

Carefully consider the position to
which our brother is about to be
raised.
Our Lord Jesus Christ, who was sent
by the Father to redeem the human
race,
in turn sent the twelve apostles into the
world.
These men were filled with the power
of the Holy Spirit
to preach the Gospel
and gather every race and people into
a single flock
to be guided and governed in the way
of holiness.
Because this service was to continue to
the end of time,
the apostles selected others to help
them.
By laying on of hands
which confers the sacrament of orders
in its fullness,
the apostles passed on the gift of the
Holy Spirit
which they themselves had received
from Christ.
In that way, by a succession of bishops
unbroken from one generation to the
next,
the powers conferred in the beginning
were handed down,
and the work of the Saviour lives and
grows in our time.
In the person of the bishop,
with his priests around him,
Jesus Christ, the Lord, who became

High Priest for ever,
is present among you.
Through the ministry of the bishop,
Christ himself continues to proclaim
*   the Gospel*
and to confer the mysteries of faith on
*   those who believe.*
Through the fatherly action of the
*   bishop,*
Christ adds new members to his body.
Through the bishop's wisdom and
*   prudence,*
Christ guides you in your earthly
*   pilgrimage toward eternal*
*   happiness.*
Gladly and gratefully, therefore, receive
*   our brother*
whom we are about to accept into the
*   college of bishops*
by the laying on of hands.
Respect him as a minister of Christ
and a steward of the mysteries of God.
He has been entrusted with the task of
*   witnessing to the truth of the Gospel*
and fostering a spirit of justice and
*   holiness.*
Remember the words of Christ spoken
*   to the apostles:*
'Whoever listens to you listens to me;
whoever rejects you rejects me,
and those who reject me reject the one
*   who sent me.'*

And to the **candidate**:

You, dear brother, have been chosen by
*   the Lord.*
Remember that you are chosen from
*   among men*
and appointed to act for men and
*   women in relation to God.*
The title of bishop is one not of honour
*   but of function,*
and therefore a bishop should strive to
*   serve rather than to rule.*
Such is the counsel of the Master:
the greater should behave as if he were
*   the least,*
and the leader as if he were the one
*   who serves.*
Proclaim the message, whether it is
*   welcome or unwelcome;*
correct error with unfailing patience
*   and teaching.*
Pray and offer sacrifice for the people
*   committed to your care*

and so draw every kind of grace for
*   them*
from the overflowing holiness of Christ.
As a steward of the mysteries of Christ
*   in the church entrusted to you,*
be a faithful overseer and guardian.
Since you are chosen by the Father to
*   rule over his family,*
always be mindful of the Good
*   Shepherd,*
who knows his sheep and is known by
*   them*
and who did not hesitate to lay down
*   his life for them.*
As father and brother,
love all those whom God places in your
*   care.*
Love the priests and deacons who share
*   with you the ministry of Christ.*
Love the poor and infirm, strangers
*   and homeless.*
Encourage the faithful to work with
*   you in your apostolic task;*
listen willingly to what they have to
*   say.*
Never relax your concern for those
who do not yet belong to the one fold
*   of Christ;*
they too are commended to you in the
*   Lord.*
Never forget that in the Catholic
*   Church,*
made one by the bond of Christian
*   love,*
you are incorporated into the college of
*   bishops.*
You should therefore have a constant
*   concern for all the churches*
and gladly come to the aid and
*   support of churches in need.*
Attend to the whole flock
in which the Holy Spirit appoints you
*   overseer of the Church of God*
– in the name of the Father,
*   whose image you personify in the*
*   Church*
– and in the name of his Son, Jesus
*   Christ,*
*   whose role of Teacher, Priest and*
*   Shepherd you undertake*
– and in the name of the Holy Spirit,
*   who gives life to the Church of*
*   Christ*
*   and supports our weakness with his*
*   strength.*

Examination of the candidate

The candidate now stands before the ordaining bishop, who invites him to declare before the people his intention, his 'resolution' to undertake the relevant office. This is done by responding 'I am' to a series of questions:

For a deacon

> *Are you willing to be ordained for the Church's ministry*
> *by the laying on of hands*
> *and the gift of the Holy Spirit.*

> *Are you resolved to discharge the office of deacon with humility and love*
> *in order to assist the bishop and the priests*
> *and to serve the people of Christ?*

> *Are you resolved to hold the mystery of faith with a clear conscience,*
> *as the Apostle urges,*
> *and to proclaim this faith in word and action*
> *as it is taught by the Gospel and the Church's tradition?*

> *Are you resolved to maintain and deepen a spirit of prayer*
> *appropriate to your way of life*
> *and, in keeping with what is required of you,*
> *to celebrate faithfully the liturgy of the hours*
> *for the Church and for the whole world?*

> *Are you resolved to shape your way of life*
> *always according to the example of Christ,*
> *whose body and blood you will give to the people?*

For a priest

> *Are you resolved, with the help of the Holy Spirit, to discharge without fail*
> *the office of priesthood in the presbyteral order*
> *as a conscientious fellow worker with the bishops*
> *in caring for God's flock?*

> *Are you resolved to celebrate the mysteries of Christ faithfully and religiously*
> *as the Church has handed them down to us*
> *for the glory of God*

> *and the sanctification of God's people?*

> *Are you resolved to exercise the ministry of the word worthily and wisely,*
> *preaching the Gospel*
> *and explaining the Catholic faith?*

> *Are you resolved to consecrate your life to God for the salvation of his people,*
> *and to unite yourself more closely every day to Christ the High Priest*
> *who offered himself for us to the Father as a perfect sacrifice?*

For a bishop

> *Are you resolved by the grace of the Holy Spirit*
> *to discharge to the end of your life*
> *the office the apostles entrusted to us,*
> *which we now pass on to you by the laying on of hands?*

> *Are you resolved to be faithful and constant*
> *in proclaiming the Gospel of Christ?*

> *Are you resolved to maintain the deposit of faith, entire and incorrupt,*
> *as handed down by the apostles*
> *and professed by the Church everywhere and at all times?*

> *Are you resolved to build up the Church as the body of Christ*
> *and to remain united to it within the order of bishops*
> *under the authority of the successor of the apostle Peter?*

> *Are you resolved to be faithful in your obedience*
> *to the successor of the apostle Peter?*

> *Are you resolved as a devoted father to sustain the people of God*
> *and guide them in the way of salvation*
> *in cooperation with the priests and deacons who share your ministry?*

> *Are you resolved to show kindness and compassion in the name of the Lord*
> *to the poor and to strangers*
> *and to all who are in need?*

> *Are you resolved as a good shepherd to seek out the sheep who stray*
> *and to gather them into the fold of the Lord?*

Are you resolved to pray for the people
of God without ceasing,
and to carry out the duties of one who
has the fullness of the priesthood
so as to afford no grounds for reproach?

Promise of obedience*

[*for DEACON and PRIEST only]

The deacon and the priest share in the priesthood, which only the bishop has in its fullness. They are therefore co-workers with him. They symbolise their dependence on him in the priestly service by kneeling before him and placing their joined hands between the hands of the bishop.

The bishop asks:

Do you promise respect and obedience
to me
and my successors?

The candidate replies:

I do.

The bishop then says:

May God who has begun the good
work in you
bring it to fulfilment.

> **On account of their sharing**
> **in his priesthood and mission,**
> **let priests sincerely look upon**
> **the bishop as their father**
> **and reverently obey him.**
> (Lumen Gentium 28)

Invitation to prayer and Litany of the Saints

The responsibilities of the various ministries has been explained in the homily; the candidate has stated his resolve to assume these responsibilities, adding with due humility, 'with the help of God'. God's help is needed indeed, for these are serious responsibilities. The Church has already urged on each candidate the need for prayer; now the candidate is offered the support of the prayer of the Church.

The bishop now invites everyone to pray to God 'to pour out his blessing' (deacon), or 'to pour out the gifts of heaven' (priest), or 'to pour out his grace' (bishop).

It is in the ancient prayer of the Litany of the Saints that this supplication is made, many of them saints who themselves served the Church in their own time in one of these ministries. The candidate prostates himself as this great ecclesial prayer of supplication pours over him, while everyone else kneels.

Special intercessions are included in the litany:

Bless this chosen one.
    Lord, hear our prayer.
Bless this chosen one and make him
    holy. **Lord, hear our prayer.**
Bless this chosen one, make him holy,
    and consecrate him for his sacred
        duties. **Lord, hear our prayer.**

To conclude the litany, the ordaining bishop alone stands and prays:

For a deacon

Lord God, hear our petitions
and give your help to this act of our
    ministry.
We judge this man worthy to serve as
    deacon
and we ask you to bless him and make
    him holy.

For a priest

Hear us, Lord our God,
and pour out upon this servant of
    yours
the blessing of the Holy Spirit
and the grace and power of the
    priesthood.
In your sight we offer this man for
    ordination:
support him with your unfailing love.

For a bishop

Lord, be moved by our prayers.
Anoint your servant with the fullness
    of priestly grace,
and bless him with spiritual power in
    all its richness.

Laying on of hands

This great apostolic gesture, symbolising the invocation of the Spirit and the empowerment for a special task in the community, is now made.

The candidate kneels before the ordaining bishop, who alone lays his hands upon the head of the candidate. For the ordination of a bishop, all other bishops present do the same. For the ordination of deacons and priests, the concelebrating priests make this same gesture.

The solemnity of this ancient and evocative gesture is heightened by being performed in silence.

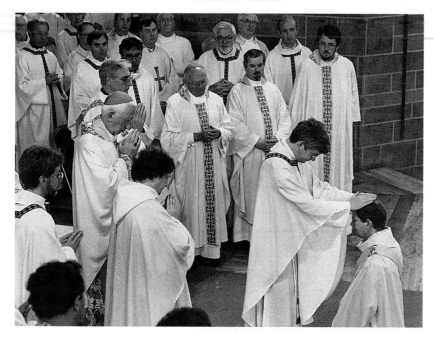

Book of the Gospels*

[for BISHOP only]*

The consecrating bishop then lays the open Book of the Gospels upon the head of the bishop-elect. Two deacons then take their place at either side of the candidate, and hold the Book of the Gospels above his head while the prayer of consecration is said.

Prayer of consecration

The candidate remains kneeling before the bishop, who extends his hands over the candidate while he says or sings the prayer of consecration.

Rather like the eucharistic prayer, there is a preliminary section which recalls the past intervention of God on humankind's behalf, related to the service the candidate will exercise in God's name for the good of the world; there is then an invocation of the Spirit, which is developed by intercessions relating to the life he must lead in terms of the ordination he is receiving. The

prayer is addressed to the Father, through the Son, imploring the gift of the Spirit.

For a deacon

*Almighty God,
be present with us by your power.
You are the source of all honour,
you assign to each his rank,
you give to each his ministry.
You remain unchanged,
but you watch over all creation and
make it new
through your son, Jesus Christ, our
Lord:
he is your Word, your power, and your
wisdom.
You foresee all things in your divine
providence
and make due provision for every age.
You make the Church, Christ's body,
grow to its full stature as a new and
greater temple.
You enrich it with every kind of grace
and perfect it with a diversity of
members
to serve the whole body in a wonderful
pattern of unity.
You established a threefold ministry of
worship and service
for the glory of your name.
As ministers of your tabernacle you
chose the sons of Levi
and gave them your blessing as their
spiritual inheritance.
In the first days of your Church
under the inspiration of the Holy
Spirit
the apostles of your Son appointed
seven men of good repute
to assist them in their daily ministry,
so that they themselves might be more
free for prayer and preaching.
By prayer and the laying on of hands
the apostles entrusted to those chosen
men the ministry of serving at
tables.
Lord,
look with favour on this servant of
yours,
whom we now dedicate to the office of
deacon,
to minister at your holy altar.
Lord,
send forth upon him the Holy Spirit,
that he may be strengthened
by the gift of your sevenfold grace*

*to carry out faithfully the work of the
   ministry.
May he excel in every virtue:
in love that is sincere,
in concern for the sick and the poor,
in unassuming authority,
in self-discipline,
and in holiness of life.
May his conduct exemplify your
   commandments
and lead your people to imitate his
   purity of life.
May he remain strong and steadfast in
   Christ,
giving to the world the witness of a
   pure conscience.
May he in this life imitate your Son,
who came, not to be served but to
   serve,
and one day reign with him in heaven.*

For a priest

*Come to our help,
Lord, holy Father, almighty and
   eternal God;
you are the source of every honour and
   dignity,
of all progress and stability.
You watch over the growing family of
   man
by your gift of wisdom and your
   pattern of order.
When you had appointed high priests
   to rule your people,
you chose other men next to them in
   rank and dignity
to be with them and help them in*
*their task;
and so there grew up
the ranks of priests and the offices of
   levites,
established by sacred rites.
In the desert
you extended the spirit of Moses to
   seventy wise men
who helped him rule the great
   company of his people.
You shared among the sons of Aaron
the fullness of their father's power,
to provide worthy priests in sufficient
   number
for the increasing rites of sacrifice and
   worship.
With the same loving care
you gave companions to your Son's
   apostles
to help in teaching the faith:
they preached the Gospel to the whole
   world.
Lord,
grant also to us such fellow workers,
for we are weak and our need is great.
Almighty Father,
grant to this servant of yours
the dignity of the priesthood.
Renew within him the Spirit of
   holiness.
As a co-worker with the order of
   bishops
may he be faithful to the ministry
that he receives from you, Lord God,
and be to others a model of right
   conduct.
May he be faithful in working with
   the order of bishops,
so that the words of the Gospel may
   reach the ends of the earth,
and the family of nations,
made one in Christ,
may become God's one, holy people.*

For a bishop

The principal consecrator alone sings or says:

*God the Father of our Lord Jesus
   Christ,
Father of mercies and God of all
   consolation,
you dwell in heaven,
yet look with compassion on all that is
   humble.
You know all things before they come
   to be;*

by your gracious word
you have established the plan of your
Church.
From the beginning
you chose the descendants of Abraham
to be your holy nation.
You established rulers and priests,
and did not leave your sanctuary
without ministers to serve you.
From the creation of the world
you have been pleased to be glorified
by those who you have chosen.

All the consecrating bishops join in reciting this next part of the prayer:

So now pour out upon this chosen one
that power which is from you,
the governing Spirit
whom you gave to your beloved Son,
Jesus Christ,
the Spirit given by him to the holy
apostles,
who founded the Church in every
place to be your temple
for the unceasing glory and praise of
your name.

The principal consecrating bishop continues alone:

Father, you know all hearts.
You have chosen your servant for the
office of bishop.
May he be a shepherd to your holy
flock,
and a high priest blameless in your
sight,
ministering to you night and day;
may he always gain the blessing of
your favour
and offer the gifts of your holy Church.
Through the Spirit who gives the grace
of high priesthood
grant him the power
to forgive sins as you have commanded,
to assign ministries as you have
decreed,
and to loose every bond by the
authority which you gave to your
apostles.
May he be pleasing to you by his
gentleness and purity of heart,
presenting a fragrant offering to you,
through Jesus Christ, your Son,
through whom glory and power and
honour are yours
with the Holy Spirit
in your holy Church
now and for ever.

Anointing of the Bishop's head*

*[*for BISHOP only]*

The newly consecrated bishop is now anointed on the head with chrism, sign of his sharing in the high priesthood of Christ:

God has brought you to share the high
priesthood of Christ.
May he pour out on you the oil of
mystical anointing
and enrich you with spiritual blessings.

Presentation of the Book of the Gospels*

*[*for BISHOP only]*

The Book of Gospels, which was held over the head of the bishop-elect during the prayer of consecration, and which has been safely guarded by one of the deacons during the anointing with chrism, is now passed to the consecrating bishop, who presents it to the newly-anointed bishop saying:

Receive the Gospel
and preach the word of God
with unfailing patience
and sound teaching.

Investiture

The newly ordained are now invested with symbols of their priestly office: above all the distinctive vestments which mark the differing but complementary roles they will have in the celebration of the liturgy.

For a **deacon**, the stole (worn by the deacon in the distinctively diagonal way, across one shoulder) and the dalmatic; for the **priest**, the stole (now worn around the neck) and chasuble; for the **bishop**, ring, mitre and pastoral staff.

At the investiture of a bishop, the consecrating bishop himself places the ring on the newly ordained bishop's ring finger, saying:

Take this ring, the seal of your fidelity.
With faith and love protect the bride
of God, his holy Church.

Similarly he places the mitre on the newly ordained bishop's head, in silence.

As he hands the newly ordained bishop his pastoral staff, the consecrating bishop says:

> Take this staff as a sign of your pastoral office:
> keep watch over the whole flock
> in which the Holy Spirit has appointed you
> to shepherd the Church of God.

Anointing of the Priest's hands*

[*for PRIEST only]

The newly ordained is now anointed with chrism. As for the anointing of the bishop's head (see page 138) this is a sign of his sharing in the high priesthood of Christ. But because the bishop alone shares the fullness of the priesthood entrusted by Christ, and the priest is the bishop's co-worker, it is the priest's hands, through which he will administer the sacraments on the bishop's behalf, that are anointed.

> The Father anointed our Lord Jesus Christ
> through the power of the Holy Spirit.
> May Jesus preserve you to sanctify the Christian people
> and to offer sacrifice to God.

Presentation

If the investiture provides the newly ordained with the vestments appropriate to their office, they now receive in this presentation the essential 'tools' of their ministry.

As the ordaining bishop places the Book of the Gospels into the hands of the **deacon**, he says:

> Receive the Gospel of Christ,
> whose herald you now are.
> Believe what you read,
> teach what you believe,
> and practice what you teach.

During the ordination of a **priest**, it is at this moment that the gifts are presented. The deacon prepares bread on the paten, wine in the chalice, and brings these to the ordaining bishop who presents them to the newly ordained priest, saying:

> Accept from the holy people of God
> the gifts to be offered to him.
> Know what you are doing,
> and initiate the mysteries you celebrate.

For a **bishop**, it is at this moment that the newly ordained bishop is led to his chair, his *cathedra*, the symbol of his teaching authority.

Kiss of peace

The final symbolic gesture in the rite of ordination is the kiss of peace, sign of the essential unit of the priesthood of Christ, sign of the differing roles shared in the service of the one Church.

THE LITURGY OF THE EUCHARIST

The Liturgy of the Eucharist continues in the usual way, with the following adaptations:

For a **deacon**

There may be several deacons, but the newly ordained deacon is the one who assists the bishop during the Eucharist.

In particular, the newly ordained deacon should assist the distribution of communion.

For a **priest**

The chalice has already been prepared, so this is omitted.

In **all ordinations** if Eucharistic Prayer I is used; the prayer *Father accept this offering* is adapted as follows:

> *Father, accept this offering*
> *from your whole family*
> *and from the one you have chosen for*
> *the order of deacon/priest/bishop.*
> *Protect the gifts you have given him,*
> *and let him yield a harvest worthy of*
> *you.*

CONCLUDING RITE

The bishop has been ordained to be one of the great sacramental signs of God's blessing on his people; now, for the first time as their bishop, he voices that blessing:

> *Lord God,*
> *you care for your people with kindness,*
> *you rule them with love.*
> *Give your Spirit of wisdom*
> *to the bishops you have made teachers*
> *and pastors.*
> *By advancing in holiness*
> *may the flock become the eternal joy of*
> *the shepherds.*
> ***Amen.***
> *Lord God,*
> *by your power you allot us*
> *the number of our days and the*
> *measure of our years.*
> *Look favourably upon the service we*
> *perform for you,*

> *and give true, lasting peace in our*
> *time.*
> ***Amen.***
> *Lord God,*
> *now that you have raised me to the*
> *order of bishops*
> *may I please you in the performance of*
> *my office.*
> *Unite the hearts of people and bishop,*
> *so that the shepherd may not be*
> *without the support of his flock,*
> *or the flock without the concern of its*
> *shepherd.*
> ***Amen.***
> *May almighty God bless you . . .*

The Ritual does give an alternative blessing, where this is given by the consecrating bishop rather than the newly ordained bishop. This would seem more appropriate where the consecrating bishop is the archbishop; or where the bishop has not been ordained to serve a particular community:

> *May the Lord bless you and keep you.*
> *He chose to make you a bishop for his*
> *people:*
> *may you know happiness in this*
> *present life*
> *and share unending joy.*
> ***Amen.***
> *The Lord has gathered his people and*
> *clergy in unity.*
> *By his care and your stewardship*
> *may they be governed happily for*
> *many years.*
> ***Amen.***
> *May they be obedient to God's law,*
> *free from hardships, rich in every*
> *blessing,*
> *and loyally assist you in your ministry.*
> *May they be blessed with peace and*
> *calm in this life*
> *and come to share with you*
> *the fellowship of the citizens of heaven.*
> ***Amen.***

CELIBACY

Because of this discipline of celibacy, (see official texts in right-hand margin column), during the ordination as a deacon there is an additional rite of commitment to celibacy. Immediately after the homily, the candidate comes and stands before the bishop, who addresses him in these or similar words:

By your own free choice you seek to enter the order of deacons. You shall exercise this ministry in the celibate state, for celibacy is both a sign and a motive of pastoral charity, and a special source of spiritual fruitfulness in the world. By living in this state with total dedication, moved by a sincere love for Christ the Lord, you are consecrated to him in a new and special way. By this consecration you will adhere more easily to Christ with an undivided heart; you will be more freely at the service of God and mankind, and you will be more untrammelled in the ministry of Christian conversion and rebirth. By your life and character you will give witness to your brothers and sisters in faith that God must be loved above all else, and that it is he whom you serve in others.

Therefore, I ask you:

In the presence of God and the Church, are you resolved, as a sign of your interior dedication to Christ, to remain celibate for the sake of the kingdom and in lifelong service to God and mankind?

The candidate replies:

I am.

To which the bishop responds:

May the Lord help you to persevere in this commitment.

CELIBACY

A candidate for the permanent diaconate who is not married and likewise a candidate for the priesthood, is not to be admitted to the order of diaconate unless he has, in the prescribed rite, publicly before God and the Church undertaken the obligation of celibacy, or unless he has taken perpetual vows in a religious institute.
(CANON Law 1037)

All the ordained ministers of the Latin Church, with the exception of permanent deacons, are normally chosen from among men of faith who live a celibate life and who intend to remain celibate 'for the sake of the kingdom of heaven' [Matthew 19:12].

Called to consecrate themselves with undivided heart to the Lord and to the affairs of the Lord' [1 Corinthians 7:32],

they give themselves entirely to God and to men. Celibacy is a sign of this new life to the service of which the Church's minister is consecrated; accepted with a joyous heart celibacy radiantly proclaims the Reign of God.
[Rite of Ordination of Priests, 16]
(Catechism 1579).

ACKNOWLEDGEMENTS

All Bible quotations are taken from *The Jerusalem Bible*, published and © copyright 1966, 1967, 1968 Darton, Longman & Todd Ltd and Doubleday & Co Inc, and used by permission of the publishers, Darton, Longman & Todd Ltd, 1 Spencer Court, 140-142 Wandsworth High Street, London, SW18 4JJ.

Excerpts from the English translation of *Rite of Confirmation, Rite of Penance, Rite of Marriage, Rite of Baptism, Rite of Ordination of Deacons, Priests and Bishops, Rite of Anointing and the Pastoral Care of the Sick* and excerpts from the English translation of *The Roman Missal* are © copyright International Committee on English in the Liturgy, Inc, 1522 K Street, NW, Suite 1000, Washington DC 20005-1202, USA. All rights reserved. Used by permission.

The extracts from *The Code of Canon Law* are translated by the Canon Law Society of Great Britain & Ireland and published by HarperCollins Liturgical Publications, 77-85 Fulham Palace Road, Hammersmith, London, W6 8JB. Used by permission.

The extracts from the Catechism are used by permission of Geoffrey Chapman/Cassells Plc, Wellington House, 125 Strand, London, WC2R 0BB.

The extracts from *The Documents of Vatican II* were translated by Austin Flannery and taken from *The Catechism of the Catholic Church*. Used by permission of Dominican Publications, 42 Parnell Square, Dublin, Ireland.

Every effort has been made to trace the owners of copyright material contained in this publication. Pardon is sought and apology made if the contrary be the case, and a correction will be made in any reprint of this book.

SONG TWO — AVE MARIA

1. Ave Maria, most favoured one.
You have been chosen to bear God's Son.
He will be Jesus, ruler divine.
His reign will last till the end of all time.

Solo 2. My spirit sings of my glorious Lord.
I am His servant, I hear His word.
Let all this happen just as you say.
I will give thanks for God's wonderful way.

3. Praise to the Father, His will be done.
God in His wisdom sending His Son.
Jesus the Saviour, ruler divine.
His reign will last till the end of all time.

At this time the country where Mary and Joseph lived was part of the Roman Empire. The Roman Emperor Augustus, wanted to have a list of all the people in the land, so he ordered everyone to return to their family's hometown to enter their names in a register. This meant that Joseph and Mary had to travel a long way from Nazareth near the Sea of Galilee, to Bethlehem, near the city of Jerusalem. The journey was slow and difficult because Mary's baby was almost due to be born.

SONG THREE — ROCKY ROAD

1. Rocky, rocky, a rocky road, weary dusty old day.
Rocky, rocky, a rocky road, still keeps stretching away.

2. Rocky, rocky, a rocky road, hazy distant town.
Rocky, rocky, a rocky road, sun keeps burning down.

3. Miles and miles have passed today, many more lie ahead.
Pacing to the rhythm of a donkey's weary tread.

4. Rocky, rocky, a rocky road, weary dusty old day.
Rocky, rocky, a rocky road, still keeps stretching away.

When at last Joseph and Mary reached Bethlehem their troubles were not over. So many people had come to register their names that every house was full and every bed was taken. Night was falling and Joseph and Mary could find nowhere to stay.

SONG FOUR   WALKING

1.   Walking, walking, searching everywhere.
No-one seems to have a room to spare.
Keep on walking, trying every inn.
Won't you help us, please may we come in?

We're so tired, we've come such a long way.
Do you have a place where we can stay?

2.   Walking, walking, far away from home.
Feeling very lost and all alone.
Keep on walking, weary as can be.
Not one friendly face for us to see.

We're so tired, we've come such a long way.
Do you have a place where we can stay ?

3.   Walking, walking, searching through the town.
Day is done, the sun is going down.
Keep on walking, asking once again
For a simple room in Bethlehem.

We're so tired, we've come such a long way.
Do you have a place where we can stay ?

The only shelter that could be found for Joseph and Mary in crowded Bethlehem, was a stable where animals were kept. In this humble place Mary gave birth to the Son of God. As was the custom, she wrapped the new-born baby in a long cloth called swaddling clothes. A manger full of hay for the animals made a bed for the baby.

Alison Hedger

The
Christmas Story

INSPECTON COPY

Alison Hedger

by Mark Golding
Arranged and edited by Alison Hedger

The Biblical Nativity Story retold in narration and songs

PUPIL'S BOOK

Contains the narration and the song words

The Teacher's Book, Order No. GA10953, contains piano accompaniment,
chord symbols, recorder and percussion parts as necessary.
The optional second vocal parts are to be learnt by rote.

A matching tape cassette of the music for rehearsals and performances is also available,
Order No. GA10972, side A with vocals included and side B with vocals omitted.

© Copyright 1994 Golden Apple Productions
A division of Chester Music Limited
8/9 Frith Street, London W1V 5TZ

Order No. GA10967

ISBN 0-7119-4324-9

THE CHRISTMAS STORY

Nearly two thousand years ago, God sent His Son to be born on earth as a helpless baby. He was not born in a palace, but in a stable, a mere animal shelter. His bed was a manger. Although Jesus is God's Son, He is also one of us. The time of His coming is called Christmas.

SONG ONE   THE CHRISTMAS STORY

1.   We're going to tell the Christmas story.
Now listen and let the tale unfold.
We're going to sing of God's great glory,
For the Christmas story's the greatest ever told.

    It's a story of wonder, a story of goodness,
A story we know is true.
It's a story of starlight, angels and shepherds,
And Jesus our Saviour born in a stable.

2.   We're going to tell the Christmas story.
How Mary listened to God's call.
How Jesus our Saviour came in glory,
And was born a child on earth to save us all.

    It's a story of hardship when Mary and Joseph
Travelled to Bethlehem.
It's a story of God's Son born in a stable.
Shepherds and wise men knelt down before Him.

3.   We're going to tell the Christmas story.
A star shone in the sky to be a sign.
Then angels sang a song of glory,
For Jesus Christ was born at Christmas time.

    For Jesus Christ was born at Christmas time.

Long ago when Herod was king of Judea, (in the land we now call Israel), God sent His messenger the Angel Gabriel, to a young woman who lived in a town called Nazareth. Her name was Mary and she was going to marry a carpenter called Joseph. Gabriel told Mary that she would give birth to a baby boy called Jesus, and that He would be God's own Son.

SONG FIVE   LULLABY

Solo Mary 1. Hush, hush, my little child,
Now close your sleepy eyes.
I'll keep you warm and safe from every harm.
I'll watch you through the night
And hold your tiny hand.
I'll love you as lie there asleep in my arms.

**Solo
Joseph** 2. Hush, hush, my little child,
Breathe gently as you rest.
Your cradle is a manger full of hay.
Your mother's at your side,
And I am close at hand.
So dream your peaceful dreams until dawning of day.

All 3. God has made mountains that reach to the sky,
The seas and the valleys so wide.
But greatest of all is this miracle boy.
A baby asleep at our side.

All 4. Hush, hush, my little child,
Sleep soundly through the night,
For soon the waiting world will see your star.
But we will keep you close, our precious little one.
There's nothing that will harm you.
So sleep in our arms.

In the fields outside Bethlehem shepherds were keeping watch over their sheep through the long night. Suddenly an angel of God stood before them, and the splendour of the Lord shone around them.

The shepherds were terrified, but the angel said "Do not be afraid. I bring good news of great joy which is for all people. Today in Bethlehem, a Saviour has been born. You will find the baby wrapped in swaddling clothes and lying in a manger."

Many more angels appeared, lighting up the sky. The shepherds heard them praising God and saying "Glory to God in the highest heaven, and on earth His peace to everyone."

SONG SIX   GLORIA

1.   Glory to God in the highest,
   This night of the Saviour's birth.
   Peace to all people on earth.

2.   Glory to God in the highest,
   Good news of great joy we bring.
   Welcome the birth of your King.

3.   You will find Him very close by,
   Asleep in a manger He lies.

4.   Glory to God in the highest,
   This night of the Saviour's birth.
   Peace to all people on earth.

The shepherds quickly went to Bethlehem and found their way to Mary and Joseph. The baby Jesus was lying in a manger, just as they had been told. When the shepherds saw Jesus they were very excited and told everyone what the angel had said and all who heard the story were astonished.

A bright new star appeared in the sky and wise men, guided by this star, travelled to Bethlehem.

SONG SEVEN   TRAVELLING ON

1.   Three wise men from distant lands,
   Travelling on, travelling on,
   Over plains and desert sands,
   Under the heat of the sun.
        Travelling on, travelling on,   (*second voices only*)
   Under the heat of the sun.

2.   Three wise men with gifts to bring,
   Travelling on, travelling on,
   Searching for a baby King,
   Follow the light of the star.
        Travelling on, travelling on,   (*second voices only*)
   Follow the light of the star.

3.   We're searching, we're searching,
    We're searching for our King.

4.   Three wise men from distant lands,
    Travelling on, travelling on,
    Over plains and desert sands,
    Under the heat of the sun.
        Travelling on, travelling on,   (*second voices only*)
    Under the heat of the sun.

The star seemed to stop and shine down on the place where the baby Jesus lay. Rejoicing the wise men entered the stable and found the baby with Mary His mother. They bowed down and worshipped Him, and gave Him their gifts of gold, frankincense and myrrh.

SONG EIGHT   NOW IS THE TIME

1.   Now, now is the time to sing.
    Sing, sing of the joy that is Christmas time.
    One Child who was born for all of us.
    One star that will shine both far and near.
        Ring, ring out the bells across the world,
        Now Jesus the Saviour is here.

2.   Peace, peace has come to our world.
    Joy, filling our hearts at this Christmas time.
    Life given by God to everyone.
    Love born as a Child to set us free.
        Ring, ring out the bells across the world,
        Now Jesus the Saviour is here.

3.   Sing, sing Him a song of peace.
    Give, give Him your love at this Christmas time.
    Tell, tell of His care for everyone.
    Shine, Light of the world both far and near.
        Ring, ring out the bells across the world,
        Now Jesus the Saviour is here.

Our Christmas story is now complete. Truly a story of wonder. But the birth of Jesus was just the beginning, for this tiny child grew up into a man who brought the light of God's love to all people of all nations. Jesus Christ was born on that special Christmas night long ago, and He changed the hearts and minds of people throughout the ages.

So let us celebrate together with joy in our hearts, as we re-tell the Christmas story again and again, year after year.

FINALE (Repeat)

SONG ONE   THE CHRISTMAS STORY

1. We're going to tell the Christmas story.
   Now listen and let the tale unfold.
   We're going to sing of God's great glory,
   For the Christmas story's the greatest ever told.

   It's a story of wonder, a story of goodness,
   A story we know is true.
   It's a story of starlight, angels and shepherds,
   And Jesus our Saviour born in a stable.

2. We're going to tell the Christmas story.
   How Mary listened to God's call.
   How Jesus our Saviour came in glory,
   And was born a child on earth to save us all.

   It's a story of hardship when Mary and Joseph
   Travelled to Bethlehem.
   It's a story of God's Son born in a stable.
   Shepherds and wise men knelt down before Him.

3. We're going to tell the Christmas story.
   A star shone in the sky to be a sign.
   Then angels sang a song of glory,
   For Jesus Christ was born at Christmas time.

   For Jesus Christ was born at Christmas time.

ISBN 0-7119-4324-9